How could they?

How long had this ~~be~~ [gone?] ~~exist~~ence? Elizabeth lo~~oked back over~~ weeks of pretence, of secrecy. Humiliation followed pain. When had Dan ceased to love her, begun to love Karen? She thought of past tenderness and shivered. Had he often kissed her, wishing she were Karen?

She turned her face against the slim trunk of one of the trees, moaning silently under her breath. Again the stark realisation of betrayal struck home.

Dan and Karen!

Dear Reader

Autumn's here and the nights are drawing in – but when better to settle down with your favourite romances? This month, Mills & Boon have made sure that you won't notice the colder weather – our wide range of love stories are sure to warm the chilliest of hearts! Whether you're wanting a rattling good read, something sweet and magical, or to be carried off to hot, sunny countries – like Australia, Greece or Venezuela – we've got the books to please you.

Enjoy!

The Editor

Charlotte Lamb was born in London in time for World War II, and spent most of the war moving from relative to relative to escape bombing. Educated at a convent, after school she went to work at the Bank of England. She married a journalist, and now has five children. The family lives in the Isle of Man.

Charlotte Lamb has written over a hundred books, most of them for Mills & Boon.

Recent titles by the same author:

KINGFISHER MORNING
FORBIDDEN FRUIT
FLORENTINE SPRING

A FAMILY AFFAIR

BY

CHARLOTTE LAMB

MILLS & BOON LIMITED
ETON HOUSE 18–24 PARADISE ROAD
RICHMOND SURREY TW9 1SR

*First published in Great Britain 1974
by Mills & Boon Limited*

© *Charlotte Lamb 1974*

*Australian copyright 1992
Philippine copyright 1992
This edition 1992*

ISBN 0 263 77802 9

*Set in Plantin 11 on 12½ pt.
01-9211-40160*

Typeset in Great Britain by County Typesetters, Kent

Made and printed in Great Britain

CHAPTER ONE

AFTER a chill and bitter spring, summer came suddenly, in mid-June, without warning. The leaden skies turned a deep and burning blue, the sun shone without a pause day after day, the frozen buds of the roses opened and fat, furry bees bumbled to and fro in the scented air.

Elizabeth Seaton locked up the village library at six o'clock during this period of halcyon weather, and walked down the path to the stile leading into Three Elms Field.

A pair of swifts were skimming over the village pond, their outlines etched dramatically against the blue of the sky. Elizabeth perched on the stile for a moment to watch their acrobatics. Their return each year was a large part of summer's pleasure for her.

The hum of an engine rose above the bird-sweet sounds of the lane. She lazily turned her head in time to recognise the car, and leapt down, waving violently. The driver was staring straight ahead. In a flash of steely blue the car spun round the corner and was gone. She stood, staring after it, feeling as hurt and disappointed as a child, then she shrugged. Dan hadn't seen her or he would have stopped, and anyway it was a perfect evening for a walk through the fields. She would see Dan later, when he came to pick her up for their visit to the cinema.

She climbed back over the stile and began the walk home, careful to keep on the narrow, mown footpath near the hedge which skirted the sea of bearded barley waving so pliably in the evening breeze.

Dan was preoccupied lately. He had a lot on his mind now that he was managing director of Woodham Electronics, especially since his grandfather, Jonas Woodham, the retiring chairman of the board, was still very much in evidence, keeping an eagle eye upon the way Dan ran things. Jonas was a hard taskmaster. One slip, and Dan would find himself in hot water. Jonas might have retired officially, but he still kept his finger very firmly on the pulse of the firm.

Only yesterday her father had laughingly complained about Jonas's insistence on knowing every detail of the everyday business of the firm. 'I'm sorry for Dan—the old man is on his back twenty-four hours a day,' he had said. 'At least the rest of us can get away from Jonas outside working hours. Dan has him all day, every day.'

Elizabeth's heart had thumped when James Seaton, smiling, had looked at her and said, 'When you and Dan are married, love, I should keep the old man out of Dan's hair as much as you can.'

It was still unbelievable to her that she should be

going to marry the great Dan Woodham. She woke up each morning with a leap of the pulses at the thought of it.

There had been a close link between the Seatons and the Woodhams ever since the original partnership was set up. Jonas Woodham had some brilliant ideas about making electronic equipment, and although it was Thomas Seaton who put up most of the original capital, Jonas had always been the dominating partner.

Thomas died of a heart attack when he was forty, leaving Jonas to run the firm alone. James Seaton, inheriting his father's estate, had inherited, too, his easy-going, pliable nature. He, like his father before him, had been more than content to leave the management of the business to Jonas. 'I'm not management material,' he had said cheerfully to his wife on more than one occasion. While he drew a substantial income from the firm, putting in a token number of hours each week, he was happy.

His wife's irritation with him had been tempered, recently, by her daughter's engagement to Dan. Mary Seaton was ambitious for her children. Elizabeth had delighted her with the news.

Of course, the two families had been brought up together, and since Dan's parents had died in a car crash when he was small, the Seaton home had been for a long time the one place where he could enjoy a normal family life.

Arrogant, domineering, the image of his grandfather, Dan had ruled the Seaton children as confidently as he now ruled the factory. Elizabeth, more her mother's child than her father's, had not had red hair for nothing. Her green eyes would flash angrily as Dan laid down the law, and she would go out of her way to defy him, despite the age gap of ten years between them. When, at six years old, she had climbed up the apple tree and refused to come down when Dan came up to fetch her, she could remember him smacking her hard, and could remember, too, that she had bitten his hand in retaliation. Dan had yelped, then stared at her, black-browed, before beginning to laugh. Shoulders hunched, like a spitting kitten, she had glared up at him before beginning to giggle herself. Dan had carried her off under his arm to buy ice-cream, and the little scene had ended happily.

When he began to date girls, Elizabeth, secretly a little jealous, had teased him and made fun of his choice. Then Dan went off to university, and later Elizabeth left school and went off to London to train as a librarian. London, at first new and exciting, soon began to bore her. It was too big, too remote. When she was qualified she came back to the village of Abbot's Mill, to run the small library housed in a prefabricated hut near the church, turning her back on prospects of promotion without a qualm.

Her mother, whose ambitions for her children were all the stronger because of her hidden disappointment in her husband, had been unable to understand her. 'Why bury yourself down here,

Liz? You could work anywhere!'

Mary Seaton found country life dull. She longed to live in a town, and only her half-impatient, half-protective love for her husband kept her chained to the quiet routine of Abbot's Mill.

Soon after returning home Elizabeth had met Dan again. It was a blinding revelation. The possessive instinct which had made him a childhood tyrant was now cloaked by charm and assurance, but, like the rock beneath a bed of flowers, it still underlay his every word. He turned it upon Elizabeth, and she dazedly found herself engaged within six short weeks.

The engagement had surprised and delighted both families. Jonas, bending his grim old face to kiss Elizabeth, had said, 'I didn't think the lad had so much sense. You won't let him rule the roost, will you? Not with that red hair.' And a wry smile had touched his mouth. 'You were always a little spitfire. Take my advice – keep Dan guessing. He's altogether too sure of himself.'

Elizabeth had surprised him by saying shrewdly, 'You would like to see him taken down a peg or two, Jonas?' No one ever called him by any other name, despite his great age, and time had given the name a dignity, almost as though it were a title. Behind his back he was often referred to as the Old Man, of course, and he knew it.

So now he said, peering bright-eyed at her, 'The Old Man resenting his young successor? Eh? Well, perhaps. That may be part of it, but also it would be good for Dan to be shaken in his impression of himself as the man with the golden touch, the irresistible, unbeatable Daniel Woodham.'

She had laughed at him, affectionately. 'Oh, he's a chip off the old block, Jonas, we all know that. Did your wife put you in your place then? Was she good for your soul?'

He had sighed. 'No, no, my dear. Poor woman, she was too gentle for me. That's why I'm glad Dan is marrying you. A little spirit in a woman makes all the difference to a marriage. It would never do for Dan to marry a girl who would be his doormat.'

Dan had been urgent for a brief engagement, and Elizabeth, for all her wish to be level-headed, was too much in love to think for herself. It was, therefore, a surprise and a shock when her father, for the first time in her life, put his foot down and insisted that she wait a year before she married.

Dan had been astonished, impatient, finally angry. 'What's the point? It isn't as if we were strangers! We've known each other long enough, heaven knows!'

Smiling blandly, James had said, 'I know, my dear Dan, but Elizabeth is ten years younger than you—I want to be certain this is the right decision.'

Dan had eyed him coolly, wondering if James Seaton was using Elizabeth as a weapon against him. Despite James's apparent lack of ambition, Dan had sometimes suspected that there was some hidden resentment in the older man. After all, he had been with the firm for thirty years, and had been passed over for the plum job just when he might have expected that Jonas would hand over the management to him. Dan could not believe that any man could view such a situation lightly. His own energy and ambition blinded him to James's contentment.

Elizabeth had tried to persuade her father to change his mind, but she found him oddly immovable. It occurred to her that Jonas and James had conspired together, but she had dismissed the idea. Jonas was so pleased by the engagement. Surely he would not have tried to put obstacles in their path?

Elizabeth would not consider going ahead against her father's wishes. Dan, when he cooled down, was persuaded to agree to a year's delay, and they settled down to wait as patiently as possible.

Their wedding was now only three months away, and already Mrs Seaton was hard at work planning the occasion. Sometimes Elizabeth felt quite frightened when she thought ahead. Her mother's ideas seemed to grow larger every day. The guest list was enormous, the many tasks involved staggering.

The only ray of light was the thought of finally being Dan's wife, and at times Elizabeth felt that even that small candle of hope grew dim. Dan was so busy lately. She saw so little of him. The firm was snowed under with orders. Dan worked late every other night. When they did meet, he seemed abstracted and impatient, as though he found it hard to bring his mind back to her level. His temper was irritable. At times she almost wondered if he still loved her. He seemed remote, scarcely even kissing her goodnight on occasions.

She paused, deep in thought, staring at a small clump of fragile, scarlet poppies, tossing wildly in the wind against the golden barley.

This long engagement was getting on their nerves, she told herself – that was what was wrong. It had made them strained and impatient with each other. Once they were married, everything would be fine.

She climbed over the garden wall of the Seaton house and was walking up through the vegetable garden, admiring the runner beans which were trained in orderly rows along the red brick wall at one side, when she heard a faint snoring.

Her brother Tom lay in the old garden hammock, a book flopped open over his face, one arm trailing to the ground. Above him the apple tree was studded with tiny green apples, and a green shade dappled his throat and bare arms.

Tom, who worked in the sales department at Woodhams, was a true Seaton, eager to enjoy the quiet pleasures of life, rather than waste his energy pursuing success.

She lifted the book and tweaked his nose gently.

He raised his lids and grinned. 'Hi, Liz! Another scorcher! Who wants to work on a day like this. Did you walk home again?'

Tom was very like their father, brown-haired, brown-eyed, with a smooth-skinned, pleasant, slightly round face. He was a year older than

Elizabeth and had gone straight into the firm after leaving school, where he had not shone in the classroom, although he was already a legendery hero of local cricket. The slow pace of cricket suited him. He settled down at the wicket with an air of cheerful immovability, and since he had a good eye and could hit a fair number of sixes, he had not had to expend too much energy on gaining his school colours.

His mother, with secret bitterness, had had to realise that he would never set the Thames on fire. He had settled down at Woodhams, as he had at the wicket, steady, reliable, far from spectacular.

Elizabeth loved him dearly, and smiled down at him now with a teasing affection. 'Lazybones! Have you been there all day?'

'No,' he said simply. 'Just for an hour. What are you doing tonight? We might play Scrabble.'

'Sorry, Dan is taking me to see a film in Canterbury,' she said gaily. 'I must rush and change before supper.'

Tom watched her walk into the house, then relapsed into his previous pose with a sigh of relief. A few flies hovered around him. The scent of roses and stocks drifted past. Tom dreamed idly.

Elizabeth found her mother in the kitchen, deftly chopping hard-boiled eggs and spring onions before blending them with mayonnaise.

Mrs Seaton looked up and smiled. The kitchen was a long, sunny room, with the windows flung open upon the garden. Pots of geraniums stood along the windowsill. A fat marmalade cat sunned himself on the doorstep, purring lazily as Elizabeth stroked his ears.

'Solomon looks pleased with himself,' she said, watching his green eyes close in delight as she tickled his head.

'He stole half a tin of sardines,' her mother informed her tartly. 'He should look pleased!'

'Naughty boy!' Elizabeth scolded gently.

Solomon gave her an offended stare and twitched his head away from her hand.

'Did you see that?' Elizabeth asked her mother. 'I'm sure he understands every word I say!'

Mrs Seaton gave her an indulgent look. 'You look hot, dear. Why don't you go up and take a shower before supper?'

'I intend to,' Elizabeth nodded, snatching a stick of celery as she passed the kitchen table.

She nibbled thoughtfully as she went upstairs. A sudden impulse made her decide to give Dan a little jolt tonight. He might be taking her for granted, she thought. She would try to look her best, startle him into noticing her again.

Cool and relaxed after her shower, she chose a new dress which she had just bought, made in a full-skirted dark green cotton, so fine that it was almost transparent in a strong light. The neckline was low and very simple. Her long, silky red hair shone against it, like a flame, and when she had wound her hair up into a chignon she clipped it into place with a matching dark green velvet bow.

Supper was almost over when the telephone rang. The family looked up, then avoided each other's eyes as Elizabeth, going pale with an instant premonition, jumped up to answer it.

Dan's voice, clipped and aloof, said, 'Sorry, but I have to go back to the factory tonight—a sudden flap in the transistor department. We'll have to shelve the film until next week.'

'I understand,' she said flatly.

There was a pause, then he asked slowly, 'What will you do?'

'Oh, wash my hair,' she said lightly. 'Don't worry about me, Dan. I'll amuse myself.'

Again a pause, then he said brusquely, 'Yes, I'm sure you will.'

With astonished anger she realised that he had hung up with that final, odd remark. She stared at the telephone dumbly for a moment, then slammed it down. Really, he was becoming impossible!

She turned to find her mother watching her anxiously, and forced a bright smile.

'Dan,' she said. 'He has to work late.'

Mrs Seaton frowned. 'Again? He seems to do nothing else lately. You must put your foot down now, Liz. I know the Woodhams—work is a disease with them.'

Elizabeth smiled in real amusement now. 'Oh, Mum! And you're always complaining because Tom isn't more like them!'

Her mother flushed. 'Yes, well! There is a happy medium. But the Woodhams take everything to extremes.' She shrugged. 'If you're at a loose end, dear, you might take Aunt Kate the book I promised to lend her. I meant to drop it in today, but I forgot.'

'Oh, of course I will – I know how much Aunt Kate loves to read the latest thriller. I wonder why dear old ladies often do love gory murders and tense spy stories?'

'Aunt Kate would murder *you* if she heard you calling her a dear old lady,' said Mrs Seaton drily.

Elizabeth laughed and set off with the book under her arm. She walked through the garden again, turning right to take the short cut which led to the Woodham house.

Jonas and Thomas Seaton had built their homes near each other, high on the slopes of a green valley some miles from their factory.

Jonas, as ambitious and decisive in this as in everything else, had built a large, handsome red-brick building, solid as a mountain, with elegant proportions in windows and doors, intended to house the large family he had expected would soon follow. His wife died only a few years later, in childbirth, and since Jonas was always too busy to consider marrying again, his son had grown up alone in the huge house, brought up by Jonas's sister Kate, who had never married.

Thomas Seaton had been more modest in his architecture. His pleasant, four-bedroomed house was just the right size for a small family, and there was a homely feel about it which was quite lacking at Whitebriars, the Woodham house.

When Elizabeth was ten years old she had been excited by the arrival at Whitebriars of two more children. Jonas's niece, Alice Harries, left a widow when her husband Bill died suddenly, had been forced to seek help from Jonas. He had promptly invited her to take up residence with him and Aunt Kate. Alice had accepted gratefully, bringing her son Toby, then twelve, and her daughter Karen, then eight, with her.

The children had been very welcome to Aunt Kate. Dan was away at university and the house took up so little of her time. She was delighted to have young voices about the place again.

The path between Whitebriars and Meadowsweet, the Seaton house, had been well worn as Toby, Karen and the two Seaton children ran back and forth, through the small copse of hazel planted by Jonas when he built the house, and which served as a natural barrier between their two gardens.

This had been their favourite playground. Then, it had seemed like a forest, the brambles loaded with delicious purple blackberries in the autumn, the hawthorn flush with white confetti-like petals in May, the ferns springing cool and green on either side of the path.

Liz remembered hiding there with Toby one hot summer day, giggling silently among the ferns, while Dan raged up and down the path looking for them to chastise them for breaking his new tennis racquet.

When he had finally gone, they had lain back, fanning themselves with plucked ferns, gazing up at the blue sky through green branches. Elizabeth could feel even now the deep sensation of incredible happiness she had felt. All around there had been a sweet, earthy scent, the smell of crushed ferns, the sound of birds singing, pigeons cooing invisibly.

Elizabeth had been the first to hear Dan, creeping towards them on silent, Indian feet. She had leapt up, calling to Toby to run, but Dan had caught him with a spring and begun to thrash him on the seat of his shorts.

She had turned and come back, panting, flinging herself at Dan, furiously beating him with her fists. 'Leave him alone, you bully!' And when Dan paused, astonished, she had shouted, 'It was an accident! We didn't mean to break your silly old racquet! We said we were sorry.'

Dan had dropped Toby, still staring at her, laughed oddly and walked away.

Toby had always been Elizabeth's chief ally and companion. They were both lively, imaginative children. Karen was rather plump, sleepy, a little inclined to weep when she was stung by a nettle or tripped over a molehill. She usually stayed with Tom and played some more placid game, like chess or draughts, while the other two climbed trees and whooped horribly, dropping down on unsuspecting travellers, like Aunt Kate, slowly making her way through the copse to visit Mrs Seaton.

Elizabeth sighed as she stopped to watch a

magpie on a rotten tree stump. How long ago childhood seemed, yet how freshly it lived in her memory.

She focussed on the magpie suddenly. One for sorrow, she thought, shuddering, then shook herself. What folly! Yet how these old country superstitions clung!

She turned to walk on, then paused again, hearing Dan's voice near at hand.

She was, she realised, on the edge of the Whitebriars garden. She could see the dazzle of sunlight beyond the last few trees. She moved softly, meaning to surprise Dan by a sudden appearance, then froze as she heard what he was saying.

'Darling, don't,' he murmured, and she felt a wild pang of pain as she heard the tenderness in his voice.

She could just see him through the screen of trees. He stood, his profile towards her, looking down at Karen. Elizabeth was bewildered, hurt, incredulous, as she realised that Dan had his arms around Karen and was holding her head against his shoulder.

'I'm sorry,' Karen said huskily. 'I have tried not to cry, Dan, but I'm so unhappy!'

'I know, darling, I know,' Dan said. He moved his cheek slowly against Karen's soft brown hair. 'But how can we tell her the truth? I can't face it, Karen. I honestly don't think she could bear it, and do we have the right to ease our own pain by hurting her? We must be brave. I know it hurts like hell, but it would hurt far more to have to tell her, wouldn't it, dear?'

'Yes, I suppose you're right,' Karen said, a harsh sob in her throat. 'It's only. . . I feel so guilty. . . knowing. . . facing her every day, not saying anything. I'm afraid she'll read it in my face. If she guessed, and we hadn't said anything!'

'I'm sure she hasn't suspected a thing,' Dan said gently. 'Dry your eyes now. Smile. We must go back to the house or someone will start asking questions.'

They began to walk away. Karen was still whispering to him. Elizabeth stood there, her eyes wide in her white, shocked face, unable to move from the spot.

Dan and Karen! It had never occurred to her that there could be anything between them but the most affectionate brother-sister relationship. They had grown up under the same roof. She had never seen anything to give her cause to suspect this!

Now she knew the reason for the many broken dates, the excuses, the abstracted behaviour which had worried her recently.

Hurt bewilderment filled her mind for some time. She could not think properly. All she could see was Dan's dark face bent over Karen, his deep voice murmuring those gently comforting words.

Then, as the first agony of grief subsided a little, she began to be angry.

How could they? How long had this secret love

been in existence? She looked back with pain over weeks of pretence, of secrecy. Humiliation followed pain. When had Dan ceased to love her, begun to love Karen? She thought of past tenderness and shivered. Had he often kissed her, wishing she were Karen?

She turned her face against the slim trunk of one of the trees, moaning silently under her breath.

There had always been some part of Dan withheld from her. He had almost seemed wary of letting her get too close. Even in the first dazzled weeks after falling in love, she had never quite known what he was thinking, confronted with his cool, dark face. He had watched her, keeping himself in hand all the time even when demanding and receiving passion, and now she felt sick as she remembered her own impulsive, generous giving of love. It was not in her nature to be coolly detached. She had fallen in love with total abandonment of self. Oh, she had teased, mocked, argued with him at times, because as Jonas had seen she was not the doormat type. But she had held back no part of her heart or mind, hidden nothing from him, unashamed if he saw clearly that she loved him with all the passion of her nature.

Had that been what Jonas had meant? Had he been warning her against allowing Dan to see how much she loved him?

She had always known that Dan was ambitious, tough-minded, unfaltering in pursuit of what he wanted. Should she have kept him at arm's length, kept him guessing, as Jonas put it? Had Dan lost interest in her once he knew he was sure of her love?

Again the stark realisation of betrayal struck home. Dan and Karen!

Somehow it seemed worse that it should be Karen, her oldest friend, her dearest, after Tom and Toby. Elizabeth had always preferred the company of the three boys to that of Karen. Her active, impulsive character took her out of Karen's more sedentary world. But they had, Elizabeth had fondly believed, become much closer friends since growing up. When Elizabeth stopped climbing trees and started enjoying pretty clothes, she had drawn nearer to Karen, and, she had thought, Karen had welcomed her friendship.

Tears were pouring down her face now. She sat down on the ground, biting her lip, struggling for control.

Again and again she went back over what she had heard, and gradually she realised that she was not being fair to them. They were obviously both far from happy. From what they had said, she was rather being protected than betrayed. They could not help it if they had fallen in love. This sort of thing happened to people without their being aware of it. Perhaps they had suddenly realised how they felt one day, had been taken by surprise by their feelings.

She scrubbed roughly across her eyes and swallowed. Her throat seemed as dry as dust.

Of course, she told herself wearily, I can't allow

this to go on – I can't let them sacrifice themselves like this. I must end this horrible mess at once.

A sharp pain pierced her. And lose Dan? her inner self asked. She put up her chin proudly. Yes, she thought. You can't lose what you don't have, and I don't have Dan any more. All I can do now is let him go with dignity.

I'll have to go to him tomorrow, tell him I heard everything, tell him that he's free.

She stood up and began walking fast back the way she had come, then stopped suddenly. How could she tell him she had overheard what he said to Karen? That would only load them both with an intolerable burden of guilt and self-reproach.

Somehow she must break the engagement without ever hinting that she suspected anything of what lay between him and Karen.

She could not yet face her family. She needed time to think. So she wandered down through the dusky fields, her eyes now dry but set in a hard stare. She hardly noticed where she went, and was surprised to find herself emerging on a narrow country lane, some miles away. She began to walk along the grass verge, watching the sky softly darken overhead. The night chorus of the birds had a sad, dying fall to her ears tonight. In the hedge the white flowers of cow-parsley moved like the ghosts of flowers, trembling to the caress of the wind. A few moths flitted around her.

She jumped as a red sports car pulled up with a screech of brakes. When she turned, half alarmed, a gay voice hailed her. 'Where are you going to, my pretty maid? Especially at this hour!'

She relaxed, smiling back. 'Toby, you idiot!'

Bright, laughing brown eyes danced back at her. 'Is that kind? Here I am, young Lochinvar himself, driving to the rescue of a benighted maid, and you call me an idiot! Hop in!'

She obeyed with a grin and the car shot away again at the same breakneck pace.

'Hey, slow down!' she protested. 'I want to arrive in one piece!'

He looked at her sideways, his face teasing. 'Scaredy cat!' But he slowed down all the same.

Toby was slim, dark, very bronzed. His dark brown hair curled tightly close to his narrow head, his ears were slightly slanting, giving him a pixy expression when he grinned. He was gay, charming, given to wild impulses but with a very kind heart. As in their childhood, he was Elizabeth's closest ally, and she knew that, if anyone could, Toby might read her mind, so she tried to look very cheerful.

She was not very successful. He was watching her in the mirror, and now he asked softly, 'What's up?'

Her pale cheeks grew pink, but she tried to smile. 'Nothing!'

He continued to watch her. 'Dan stood you up again?'

Her eyes slid sideways to try to read his expression. Did he suspect something? He was, after all, in the same house as Dan and Karen day after day. Toby had a shrewd, quick-witted mind. He was not easy to fool.

'Yes,' she said slowly, 'he had to work late tonight.'

'Dan's obsessed,' Toby said lightly. 'He lives, eats, drinks Woodhams. I enjoy my work, but I'm damned if I'd let it take over my entire life.' The laughing eyes met hers again. 'Especially with a dolly-bird like you waiting on the sidelines.'

Liz laughed without amusement. 'Thanks!'

Toby's face sobered quickly. 'Liz, what is it?' he asked seriously. 'Come on, kid, you can trust me!'

She looked at him affectionately. 'I know I can, Toby, but there's nothing to tell you.'

'I see,' he said slowly. After a pause he said cheerfully, 'I know what you need—a nice long glass of cider. Just the thing at the end of a hot day.'

He pulled off the road into the forecourt of a pretty old pub and they climbed out of the car. They drank their cider in the garden, under brightly coloured umbrellas, while the darkness thickened around them. There were strings of coloured lights wound in and out of the trees in the garden, looking like strange jewels against the soft grape-bloom of the sky.

Toby looked at her thoughtfully as he talked. 'Have you heard the latest plan? Dan is sending me to Italy for a year – he wants to have a liaison officer between Woodhams and the Italian firm we're linking up with. We have big plans to expand into Europe.' He grimaced. 'I should say, Dan has big plans. He sees himself as another Wellington, conquering Europe.'

Elizabeth's heart sank. 'Oh, Toby, I shall miss you! But it will be great fun for you.' She smiled at him. 'All those lovely dark-eyed *signorinas*!'

'I shall enjoy it,' he agreed. 'I'll come home for your wedding, of course. The wedding of the year—who could miss it?'

Her smile withered on her lips. 'Yes,' she said dully.

Toby's eyes narrowed. 'Liz?' he asked gently. 'What's wrong? Can't I help?'

She looked up and shook her head. 'No!'

He put his glass on the table and stood up. 'Well, we'd better get back now.'

They drove back through the dark lanes at a leisurely pace. The cool air rushed over her face. She sat in silence, her eyes fixed on the darkness of the trees rushing past. Her heart ached. Tears began to trickle slowly down her face. She turned her head so that Toby should not see them and surreptitiously wiped her eyes.

The car jerked to a stop outside her home. She fumbled with the door and Toby leaned across to open it for her, looking closely at her.

'For God's sake, Liz,' he said sharply. 'What is it?'

'I'm tired,' she said wearily, 'that's all.'

He put a hand under her chin and tilted her face. She met his eyes warily.

'You're a very poor liar, my girl,' he said gently. Then he kissed her on the nose. 'Well, if you won't confide in Uncle, go to bed and sleep it off. Goodnight.'

Tom opened the front door, looking flustered. She walked in with a forced smile, then stopped dead, going first white, then dark red as she saw Dan looming up behind him. Her heart lurched violently, then went on beating very fast. Tom slid discreetly away towards the stairs.

'Where the hell have you been?' Dan asked grimly. 'Your mother said you'd gone over to Whitebriars, but you never arrived.'

'I'm sorry,' she said calmly, mustering the last remnants of her self-control. 'I met Toby, and he took me for a drive.' She held out the book she had been carrying all this time. 'Here, you'd better take this with you. It's for Aunt Kate.'

Dan took it slowly, staring at her. She looked back, aching with love for him. He was a good head taller than herself, very dark and built on strong lines, his features ruggedly powerful, his blue eyes at the moment like chips of ice under the thin dark brows.

He was a man people noticed in a crowd. His arrogantly held head, his broad shoulders and look of controlled strength made him dangerously attractive to women, and a challenge to most men.

How can I bear to give him up? she thought miserably. Then her pride came to the rescue. She wouldn't hold on to a man who wished to be free.

'I thought you were working late tonight,' she said coolly.

'I was,' he retorted. 'It *is* eleven o'clock, you know. I've been waiting for you for an hour. I thought I might call in on my way home—that was how I discovered that you'd disappeared.'

Liz turned away, yawning. 'Ooh. . .I'm sorry! I'm very tired. Driving in the fresh air always makes me sleepy, and Toby had the hood up.'

'Where did he take you?'

'To the Golden Hind. We sat in the garden, drinking cider and talking. It was too warm to bear it inside. They had the coloured lanterns in the trees and there was a man playing Strauss waltzes on the piano inside. We could hear it through the open window.' She was talking too much. She could not bear the idea that he might guess at the misery inside her.

'Very romantic!' he said bitingly.

She looked at him in surprise, then a flash of temper made her retort, 'Yes, it was—very!'

There was a long pause. Dan stared at her, his brows drawn together, the blue eyes narrowed and cold as steel.

'Did Toby tell you I'm sending him to Italy?' he demanded.

She felt wildly resentful suddenly. Not content with breaking her heart, she thought, he was bent on removing her closest friend just at the time she most needed support.

'Yes,' she said hotly, 'he told me. And I think you might have waited until after we're married. I shall miss him and. . .' She felt the tears stinging her eyes. She did not know what she was saying any more. She turned towards the door, blinded by tears, and stumbled slightly.

Dan gripped her arm in a vice-like hand. 'Go on,' he said coldly. 'Go on. . .'

She shook her head. 'I'm tired. I'm going to bed,' she said childishly, self-pity flooding up inside her in a way which, later, she would find nauseating and humiliating.

Dan shook her, bending down to look at her face, his own features tight with anger.

'Finish what you were saying,' he demanded.

She helplessly shook her head again, feeling limp and drained. 'Please, Dan. I want to go to bed.' She looked up and their eyes met, each face masked and wary.

'Very well,' he said slowly. 'We'll leave it. Perhaps it would be best. There's no point in dragging things out into the open.'

Did he guess that she had discovered his secret? she wondered wildly. Had he been about to tell her the truth? Knowing Dan as she did, she knew that when he lost his temper it was like being in an earthquake. That cold control, once snapped, could become a fiery torrent. He might forget his good intentions and shout the truth from the rooftops. That must not happen. Their engagement must not end like that, or all family relations would be soured for years. It was going to cause enough trouble if she broke off the engagement herself. If Dan broke it to marry Karen, even Jonas would be bitterly angry with him.

She walked to the door with him, praying that he would not kiss her. She could not bear it if he did. That Judas kiss would sting like the brand of an iron.

He did not kiss her. He looked at her once, his face withdrawn, then said, 'Goodnight,' brusquely and was gone.

CHAPTER TWO

ON THURSDAYS the library was closed all day. Elizabeth had always enjoyed having this day off in the middle of the week. It gave her the chance to go shopping while the shops were less crowded than they always were on Saturdays, and it was pleasant to be free while most other people were working.

But on this Thursday morning she was in no mood to wander around, window-shopping, and she merely looked grim when her mother suggested they went in search of various items needed for her trousseau.

'But, Liz,' protested Mrs Seaton, 'we haven't got very much time, you know. Three months may seem long enough to you, but believe me, we need every minute of it, if we're to make sure that this wedding is as perfect as I've always dreamed it would be.'

'I know, Mum, I'm sorry, but not today,' Liz said drearily. She mentally resolved to break her engagement as soon as possible. If she delayed much longer, the consequences which would follow would seem too terrible to contemplate. Before her courage evaporated she must do the right thing.

'You haven't even chosen the design for your

wedding dress,' her mother said, unaware of the turmoil inside her daughter.

Elizabeth restlessly walked to the kitchen door. She stared without even seeing it at a latticed fence covered with white roses.

Mrs Seaton paused, frowning. Elizabeth walked out into the garden.

'What's wrong with her?' her mother demanded of the empty room. 'Whatever is wrong with her?'

Elizabeth wandered down the garden aimlessly, and sat down on a rather rickety old garden bench, staring out over the green sweep of the meadows falling away below to the village. A clump of shadowy dark green elms hid the church, but the soaring grey stone spire just appeared behind them. A heat haze shimmered over the horizon. An aeroplane droned somewhere out of sight. It was a peaceful scene, and one which seemed to mock heartlessly at the agony within her.

She heard Karen's voice from the house and stiffened. How was she going to face her and not betray her knowledge of the secret love between Dan and this girl whom she had always considered to be her friend?

Karen's footsteps were muffled by the lawn. She appeared suddenly, smiling. She was small, still slightly plump, but now it was a rounded generosity of figure which suited her and gave an appealing prettiness to her face. Her brown hair was cut short and clung to her head in soft waves. Her brown eyes, very like Toby's, beamed warmly.

'Dan gave me a lift down. I'm getting another lift from Tom, but he isn't ready yet.' She grinned. 'How to get to work in two easy stages!'

Elizabeth's smile seemed stiff, but her voice sounded normal enough, thank God. 'Isn't Dan going in to the factory this morning?'

Karen gave her an odd, sharp look. 'No,' she said slowly. 'He's taking you into Canterbury, isn't he?'

'Oh,' said Elizabeth. She looked at Karen. 'That's a pretty dress. Yellow suits you.'

'Thanks.' Karen grimaced. 'Tom said I looked like a buttercup.'

'How tactless of him,' Elizabeth said gently. 'I expect he meant it as a compliment, though.'

Karen shrugged. 'What he meant was quite clear—I'm bright and childish. Tom has always thought of me as a child.' The round curves of her small face elongated in sombre thought. 'But I'm not one,' she added to herself.

Elizabeth watched her. Yes, she thought, Karen was unhappy. She could see dark smudges beneath the brown eyes. The mouth had a weary droop which had not been there before. Pity filled her. Poor little Karen, she thought. The two years between them had always seemed far more than that. She, like Tom, had always thought of Karen as a child. Why must love be so complicated?

Tom yelled from the house and Karen turned to go, waving goodbye to Elizabeth. Then the garden was very still once more. The birds sang from tree and roof. Somewhere a grasshopper chirped.

Elizabeth suddenly heard a step behind her. Turning her head, she met Dan's cool blue eyes. She felt her face whiten involuntarily, and tried to smile, but the movement of her mouth was cold and stiff.

He pushed his hands into his pockets and surveyed her, his head tilted back, the blue eyes half hooded.

'You're very pale,' he said.

'I didn't sleep very well,' she answered quietly.

'Why not?' The words came sharply, startling her, and the lids drew back, revealing a fierce blaze in the blue eyes which suddenly seemed much brighter and more compelling.

She stood up, feeling incredibly nervous, and walked down the path which led to the copse. She felt him following her. Her pulses were leaping. She must do it now, but ludicrously, she could not find the words. It seemed stupid that she should actually feel guilty, as though it were she who were in the wrong.

She stopped on the edge of the copse, staring longingly into the cool green depths.

Taking a deep breath, she said, 'Dan, I'm sorry. I find I've been mistaken about. . .I can't marry you, Dan.' She had meant to put it far more eloquently, but when it came to it, she could only say the words starkly.

There was a long silence. She looked up at last, expecting to see relief, surprise, doubt on his face, but instead found him regarding her as bleakly as a winter day.

'May I ask the reason?' he asked in frozen politeness.

She was taken aback, bewildered. Could she have mistaken the situation, after all? Had she leapt to the wrong conclusion? Then she remembered the anguish in their voices, the misery in their faces as they clung to each other, and the faint flare of hope which had sprung up died as rapidly.

She knew that Dan had a strong sense of duty. He must be wondering, now, if she had found out about his feelings for Karen. He would be angry with himself for having hurt her. This bleak look meant nothing else.

She gathered up all her strength. He must not suspect anything. It would only ruin his chance of happiness with Karen. Guilt could poison love, and she did not want to be responsible for ruining their lives. Better for one person to be unhappy than for three people's lives to be wrecked on the jagged rocks of jealous possessiveness.

Elizabeth knew that she could not extinguish the little fire of jealousy which had been kindled inside her heart, but she would die rather than let Dan or Karen see it.

Quickly, then, she said, 'Father was right to make us wait. You swept me off my feet, Dan. But I wasn't really in love with you—I know that now. I was fond of you, of course, but I mistook that old affection for something deeper. It was. . .' she paused, searching for the word which would convince him. 'It was just a temporary madness.'

His face was quite still, as though he had turned to stone. She wished he would not stare at her like that. It had never been easy to read his thoughts, but now his expression seemed quite shuttered. He was keeping all emotion out of his eyes as deliberately as herself.

She made herself smile at him. 'That's what it was, wasn't it, Dan? For you, too, I think? Just a mistake, a midsummer madness.'

'Was it?' he asked flatly.

What more did he want? she thought wildly. She had given him his longed-for freedom. He had not had to tell her. What had he said to Karen? That he could not face the thought of telling her? Yet now, with the difficult task performed for him, he seemed grim and unyielding, as though, fantastically, he was angry with her!

She fumbled at her ring and somehow managed to drag it off. He stared at it without moving as she held it out to him.

What was the matter with him? thought Elizabeth, beginning to feel angry herself. This interview was not going as she had anticipated.

His stern mouth parted, then. Icily he asked, 'It's Toby, of course?'

Liz stared, eyes widening until her muscles hurt. What did he mean? Then she realised—of course, he wanted to reassure himself, to believe that she loved someone else. He was too proud to accept a sacrifice, even when she made no accusation. Dan, being Dan, could not believe that any girl could jilt him without good cause. If she did not know about Karen, he thought she must herself be in love with someone else.

Drowningly, she thought, well, why not? If it made it easier for him?

'Yes,' she said. 'It's Toby.'

The blue eyes blazed again. She could not read their expression, though, even now. Was that joy, relief, delight? Whatever it was, the emotion was a powerful one. She saw his face tighten against it. The muscles at the corners of his mouth were pulled in, his jaw clenched hard.

'Why not come out with it, then?' he asked slowly. 'Why beat about the bush? Do you think I was totally blind? I've suspected for a long time, but I told myself I was imagining things. I know how close you and Toby have always been. I wouldn't allow myself to believe what became more and more obvious.'

Yes, she thought, she could believe that. Dan desperately looking for some decent way out of his situation, would undoubtedly refuse to permit himself to hope that she would fall in love with someone else, and thus make it easy for him.

'I'm sorry, Dan,' she said softly. The irony might strike her as hilarious later, but she said it now with utter seriousness.

'Sorry?' He repeated the word with a strange emphasis. Dark red colour came up under his skin. Suddenly, making her jump, he snatched the ring she still held out, and flung it with a savage gesture far away into the copse.

'Oh!' she cried, in grief and horror, watching the bright sparkle of the stone fly in an arc through the shadowy air. 'Why did you do that? My lovely ring! I'll never find it again.' All the pain which she had been suppressing rose unbearably to the surface and tears sprang into her eyes.

'Everyone has their limits,' he said thickly. 'I've reached mine. Civilised behaviour, so called, is a straitjacket—I can suffer it for a time, but don't use inadequate, hypocritical little words like sorry to me, or I may break out of my nice little straitjacket, and do something we'll both regret.' Then he turned on his heel and walked away, leaving her puzzled and angry.

Why had he done that? She sat down on the grass to think. Dan had shown none of the reactions she had been expecting. She did not even know what his reaction had been. He had not tried to argue with her. He had not seemed sorry, or glad. The only definite thing she knew was that he had thrown her lovely ring away, and there had been a finality about the gesture which had hurt her deeply.

Telling her family, after that painful little scene, seemed quite simple. She broke the news that evening, at supper, when they were all together.

For a few seconds there was total silence after her stark announcement. Then her mother gave a wail. 'You can't be serious!' Then, seeing from her daughter's set face that this was exactly what she was, she went on, 'You're mad! You and Dan. . .my life's ambition. I've always wanted it. I've been planning this wedding for months. All my friends. . . I'll be the laughing-stock of the county.' Her breath caught. 'Oh, Jonas! He'll never forgive you! To jilt his grandson! The old man will hold it against us all for ever.'

Wearily, Elizabeth said, 'I'm sorry, Mother.' Will I ever stop saying those words? she thought.

'Sorry?' Mrs Seaton looked at her in mingled exasperation and disbelief. 'How could you do such a thing? Dan Woodham is the most eligible bachelor for miles. Why? I don't understand why!'

James Seaton put a hand on his wife's arm. She looked at him and he shook his head warningly at her. Biting her lip, she held back the rest of her torrent of words.

Elizabeth turned to her father, waiting for his comment. He smiled gently at her.

'Well, my dear, you have put the cat among the pigeons, and no mistake.' His bland face was curious. 'How did Dan take it? Like a Trojan, I hope?'

She looked at him sharply, sensing something behind the words that disturbed her. It was almost as if her father was secretly amused by her news.

'He didn't say much,' she said slowly. 'Of course, he accepted my decision.'

'Like a gentleman,' her father nodded, smiling. And again that little frisson ran down her spine. Did her father actually dislike Dan? She knew his

views about Jonas. Did his resentment carry on to
Dan, then?

'I should think he must be furious,' her mother
burst out. 'After all, the benefits were not all on our
side. You would take him a sizeable block of shares
in the company. Your shares would have given him
complete control, a majority holding. I'm sorry for
Dan. His plans must have been thrown into ruins.'

Elizabeth stared at her mother in frozen dismay.
She had never even thought about the financial side
of the marriage. Of course, she thought, of course!
Had that been, perhaps, his real reason for wanting
to marry her? Had all the love always been on her
side alone? She could believe Dan capable of
marrying for such a reason. He took Woodhams so
seriously.

This might very well explain his reaction when
she broke off their engagement. If he had meant to
marry her for purely business reasons, he would be
angry to have his plan upset, even if he was in love
with Karen! Dan was more than capable of keeping
business and emotion separate. He had always been
an enigma, clear-headed, tough, ambitious. No
doubt it had surprised him when he fell in love with
Karen. She could almost find it in her to be sorry
for him. She could imagine how he must have
twisted and turned, trapped in this unexpected web
of love.

For some reason it made it easier for her to see
him so clearly. It hurt far less. If he had never been
in love with her at all, she had been living in a fool's

paradise, and for all the pain she was suffering, she would be grateful later that fate had cut the thread and released her from such an uneven bargain. What if she had married Dan, and found out later that he did not love her, never had loved her? She shivered at the thought.

Later, Tom sought her out and wordlessly put an arm around her. She smiled up at him reassuringly.

'We'll weather the storm,' he told her gently.

She nodded. 'Yes. I wish I hadn't had to upset Mum so much, though.'

His grimace was wry. 'Never mind Mum. It's you that worries me. You look like death, Liz. You were never very rosy-cheeked, but now you're as white as a ghost.'

'It is a strain,' she admitted. 'But it will get better as times goes on, Tom. I feel easier in my mind.'

Tom nodded. After a pause he asked, 'Why did you break it off, Liz?'

She smiled. 'I just changed my mind. Very simple.'

He looked at her, frowning. 'I wish I believed you, love. I really wish I did.'

That Saturday Toby arrived unexpectedly, and invited her to have dinner with him at a country club of which he was a member.

'It's the cricket dance,' he said. 'Is Tom going?'

Tom, it appeared, certainly was going. His brown hair sleeked down, he joined them, unusually formal in a dark lounge suit, and winked.

'I'm all set to bowl out a few blushing maidens,' he said. 'I'm glad you're coming, Liz. Dining with Toby first?'

He and Toby exchanged silent looks of understanding. She wondered vaguely if they had conspired over this evening. It was odd that Tom had not mentioned that he was going to a dance at the club. They all belonged to it since it offered unrivalled sports facilities, and was a useful social centre for the surrounding countryside.

Had Tom invited her, she would have refused. She was feeling rather prickly at the moment, and any hint of pity made her both irritable and weepy, a state of affairs which alarmed her.

She went up to change, and dressed with deliberate care, fully intending to startle her family, and, she hoped, keep at bay all the curious, half malicious enquiries she knew she would meet from acquaintances tonight.

She had the satisfaction of seeing Toby blink as she joined him. The midnight-blue dress she wore was very sleek and clinging, the smooth curve of her neck and shoulders laid bare above the tight bodice. She had threaded a silver ribbon through her red hair and dressed it simply at the back in a smooth coil.

'You look fabulous,' Toby told her sincerely.

'Where's Tom?' she asked, smiling at him.

'He went on ahead,' he told her, taking her elbow lightly to lead her out to his car.

Over dinner, in the dimly lit dining-room, Toby

told her that Dan had given the family the news of their broken engagement.

'I'm sorry, Liz,' he added gently, watching her.

She shrugged. 'It was one of those things. Is Jonas very angry?'

He grinned. 'Livid! He fancied you himself, I think. He'll be down like the wolf on the fold tomorrow, I expect. Watch out for squalls.'

'I'm not afraid of Jonas,' she said stubbornly.

'No,' he agreed thoughtfully. 'That was why he liked you so much, I imagine. He doesn't often come up against people who are ready to stand up to him.' He glanced at her. 'Nor does Dan.'

Liz's eyes dropped to the tablecloth. She sighed. Would Karen be strong enough to stand up to Dan? Or was it that gentle pliability which attracted him, anyway? Was Jonas wrong in believing that Dan needed a strong-willed girl? After all, by his own admission, Jonas had married a gentle girl himself.

'What are you going to do now?' Toby asked her. 'Have you realised how embarrassing it's going to be for you? Seeing Dan all the time, I mean?'

She nodded. 'I might take a job in London again.' Her tone lacked enthusiasm.

'How about Italy?' suggested Toby.

She looked up, eyes wide. 'Italy?' She laughed. 'Why Italy?'

'I shall be there,' he said complacently.

She laughed. 'Toby, you're an idiot!' Then a thought struck her, and she flushed bright pink. Her eyes met his. 'Toby, has Dan said anything. . . ?'

'Plenty,' he returned succinctly. 'Mainly on the theme that he'll break my neck if I don't make you happy.'

'Oh, Toby!' She stared at him in horror. 'I *am* sorry. I used you as a cover. Dan suggested it and I accepted the idea.'

His bright eyes danced. 'Am I complaining? You might have given me a hint. I could have dropped a brick, without realizing it. Luckily, Dan took me so much by surprise that I didn't have time to put my foot in it.'

'You didn't disabuse him of the idea, then?' she asked with some anxiety.

He shook his head. Watching her closely, he asked, 'Am I to be told the real reason?'

A dimple appeared in her cheek. 'You think you're not the real reason, then?'

For a second his smile vanished, then he grinned again. 'My dear girl, I'm not a fool, even though I know I look it! You aren't in love with me—I know you too well to believe that. You feel as romantic about me as you do about the prawn salad you've just eaten.'

She laughed. 'How right you are!'

'So what's the real reason?' he insisted.

'Nothing I can talk about,' she said.

He shrugged. 'Well, that's fine with me. What about Italy, though? I can get you a job with Perini's, you know. You did some Italian at school, didn't you?'

'Two years,' she agreed. 'I'm very, very bad at it,

though. I can read it, but not speak it very well.'

'Do you think you could write brief notes in Italian on English trade descriptions? I'll need an assistant to do that. I'm sure you could manage with a good dictionary.'

'Would they accept me, though?' she asked dubiously.

Toby winked. 'Look, I've been given carte blanche to choose my own staff. This is a new, very small department I'm setting up. You'll be directly responsible to me. If I'm happy, nobody else will have the right to complain.'

'You're very kind, Toby,' she said warmly. 'Can I have time to think it over?'

He nodded. 'But hurry up! I leave next week, and you ought to travel with me.'

'Next week?' she repeated in surprise. 'So soon?'

'Liz, are you sure about breaking it off with Dan?' he asked in reply. 'Do you still feel something for him?'

Something? Elizabeth laughed bitterly inside herself, but aloud she said, 'No, Toby, I'll never marry Dan.'

'Then you'll be glad of a bolthole in Italy,' he pointed out. 'Dan is a dangerous enemy. He never gives up, you know. If he still wants you he'll bide his time, then come back to the attack when he thinks I'm safely out of the way.' He glanced at her shrewdly. 'I wonder if that's why I'm being sent to Italy? It surprised me at the time. I thought he was just getting me out from under his feet. He might have had more personal reasons.'

She smiled tightly. 'No, Toby,' she said. 'Dan wouldn't have sent you away for my sake.'

'No?' He stared at her. 'Well, you know best, I suppose.'

They had been dancing for about an hour when Dan and Karen walked into the crowded room. Elizabeth, whirling around in Toby's arms and laughing up at him as he teased her about her halting Italian, suddenly heard she muted whispering which died away as she looked round.

When she saw Dan across the room, she realised that the grapevine had already got to work.

The news of their broken engagement was already well known, and people watched avidly as Dan inclined his head with coolly impersonal courtesy.

Elizabeth and Toby smiled back in the same manner. Elizabeth trembled slightly, and felt Toby pull her closer.

'All right, love?' he asked, looking down at her gently.

She smiled. 'Fine!'

'All flags flying,' he nodded. 'Shall we give them a show for their money?' And bending his head he brushed his mouth along the warm curve of her shoulder and throat. Shaken, she jerked away, and he looked up at her, grinning. 'Hey, you're supposed to swoon!'

Her cheeks were flushed and her eyes very bright. 'Please, Toby—don't! I feel conspicuous enough already.'

Beneath his breath, he said, 'Ah, but that's the secret, you know. Never give anything away. The worse you feel, the more you must pretend you never felt better in your life. It always rains when you haven't got an umbrella, and banks never lend money to poor people.'

'Thank you, Shakespeare, and goodnight,' she retorted with angry flippancy.

He grinned. 'That's more like it! Come on, cheek to cheek,' and pulled her closer still, his face pressing against hers. Over his shoulder she briefly met Dan's icy blue eyes. He was looking quite expressionless, but again she had a strong impression that he was angry.

He was probably reflecting that if she married Toby, her block of Woodham shares would pass out of his control, she thought in bitter cynicism.

When the dance ended, Toby laughingly slid his arm around her and led her over to his sister and Dan.

'You've missed half the fun,' he said lightly.

Karen was very pale. Her eyes looked up at Elizabeth with a searching intensity.

'Hello, Karen,' Elizabeth said quietly.

Karen paused for an obvious second or two, then she answered, with a sigh, 'Hello. Enjoying yourself?'

Dan broke in sardonically, 'Obviously!'

Elizabeth's cheeks grew even more hectic red. Toby's hand tightened on her waist. He stared challengingly at Dan, and for a moment the two men faced each other with an aggressive hostility which Elizabeth had never seen from them before. Then Dan turned his head away, and Toby laughed softly.

Karen looked at her brother indignantly. 'Toby, have you been drinking?'

He laughed even more at that. 'My dear girl, certainly not! I'm just happy.'

Karen did not seem to find the spectacle of his happiness endurable. She looked down at her linked hands, her face going even more pale.

Elizabeth felt sorry for her. It gave her no pleasure to see Karen so wan and ill at ease. 'Shall we dance again?' she asked Toby.

Dan stood up abruptly, and the other three looked at him in startled surprise.

'No,' he said curtly. 'My dance, I think?'

Toby bristled visibly. 'I think *not*,' he said with emphasis.

Dan looked directly at Elizabeth. 'Why do you think we came here?' he asked a trifle contemptuously. 'There's going to be plenty of gossip anyway, but if we're seen to be on speaking terms the gossip will die a quick death.'

'Oh,' she said, suddenly very touched. 'Thank you.'

Toby sat down beside his sister. Elizabeth walked on to the floor with Dan and put her hand on his shoulder. His arm went round her waist, and as his fingers gripped her she felt a sharp sensation of pleasure deep inside her body. It felt so right.

They danced in silence for a moment. They had always danced well together, and now she wondered miserably how she could bear never to dance with him again.

He tightened his hold, and she looked up. 'Say something,' he murmured coolly. 'Smile. Look happy. Everyone is watching us.'

She forced a bright smile. 'This is very thoughtful of you, Dan.'

'Yes,' he said, 'isn't it? I didn't realise I was such a fool.' And he gave her a charming, totally false smile which did not reach his eyes.

'I'm going to Italy with Toby,' she said, out of a fierce desire to hit back, to hurt him.

His smile stayed, pinned to his lips. 'How nice for you both.'

Elizabeth smiled back, equally falsely, although she was beginning to feel very tired and it was a strain, keeping that bright, idiotic grin on her face.

'Yes,' she said. 'I think we shall enjoy it very much.'

'Are you marrying him before you go? That will be a shock for your parents. It would have to be a civil affair—there isn't time to arrange a church wedding.'

She laughed merrily, throwing back her head. 'Oh, we aren't in that much of a hurry. We'll wait until we get back to England.'

His eyes stabbed at her. 'Toby should learn from my experience. He'd do better to marry you quickly before you change your mind again. Who knows, you may meet some handsome Italian and fall for him.'

She gave him a sweet, patient look. 'I doubt it, Dan. But what about you? Perhaps you'll marry while we're in Italy.' Now, she thought, he must tell me about Karen. I've left it open to him. If he has any decent instincts, he'll tell me, and not go on pretending to be the one who was basely jilted.

He bent the cold blue eyes on her face, still smiling with his mouth. 'You may be right. I certainly don't intend to pine away for love of you. I know when I've had a lucky escape. Next time, I'll find someone who understands the meaning of the word fidelity.'

A burning anger filled her. She could no longer pretend to smile at him. Her green eyes flashed bitterly. 'Poor girl! I'm sorry for her, whoever she is!' Poor Karen, she thought. I hope she never finds out what a cold-hearted beast Dan can be be when he's crossed. My mother must have been right about his reasons for wanting to marry me. Only rage could make him say such things. It's I who've had a lucky escape. God, what a hypocrite! How dare he make this scene? When I think how he soothed Karen down, pretending that he was too soft-hearted to hurt me, when all the time he had no intention of breaking off our engagement for his own purely mercenary reasons! After we were married, perhaps he would have tried to talk her into becoming his lover. I wouldn't put it past him. How I loathe and detest him!

She smiled up at him, in command of herself once more, and saw that her shaft had gone home. He was very pale and tight-lipped. That false smile had gone.

'You were always a vicious-tongued little vixen, Liz,' he said against her ear. 'I ought to slap your face!'

She laughed. 'Just try it,' she whispered. 'Just try it!'

He was silent for a moment, then he laughed, too. His teeth closed gently on the lobe of her ear. She stiffened but made no sound of protest.

'This has been quite an evening for you,' he murmured drily. 'Toby kisses your shoulder, I bite your ear. Liz, the femme fatale. Is it exciting, causing all this stir?'

'Devastating,' she retorted flippantly as the music ended. He released her at once and they walked back to Karen and Toby side by side, both smiling.

Dan gave Toby a cool look. 'I return your partner to you intact,' he said.

'Thanks,' Toby replied curtly. He looked at Elizabeth with an enquiring lift of the eyebrows.

She smiled her reassurance. Toby saw the angry sparkle in her eyes, the lifted chin and determined angle of her head. He read the signs correctly. Whatever Dan had said to her, she was even more

determined in her decision. The wistful little droop
of her lips had quite gone. Anger had driven out
regret.

CHAPTER THREE

WHEN her parents heard her plans for the future, they were both startled and angry.

'I refuse to let you do it,' her father said in a stern voice, staring at her as though he had never seen her before. 'Go to Italy with Toby? What a ludicrous notion!'

Mrs Seaton was bright red as she burst into speech on the heels of her husband's last words. 'Are you determined to cause talk? Toby! Is that what's happened? You've decided you're in love with Toby!' Her eyes sparkled with angry condemnation. 'How could you, Liz? When Alice Harries hinted at such an idea I told her she was being absurd. I couldn't believe you would be so foolish.'

Elizabeth indignantly retorted, 'Why should it be foolish? What's wrong with Toby? I've known him for years. You've always seemed very fond of him. Why is he suddenly in your bad books?'

James Seaton spoke before his wife could erupt into further irritated frankness. Coolly, his voice silky, he said, 'My dear girl, you must be aware of the fact that Toby is jealous of Dan? He always has been—and if you fondly imagine it to be personal, you can forget it. Toby resents Dan's position in the firm. You have nothing to do with the case. He's merely using you as a weapon against Dan.'

Flushed and bright-eyed, she stared at him. 'What nonsense! I know Toby better than you do, Dad. He isn't petty-minded.'

'Far from it,' smiled James Seaton. 'He's a very ambitious and clever young man.'

The sneer in his voice cut her. 'Oh, Dad,' she said, turning away, 'I won't listen to this! I think you're doing Toby an injustice. I know you're all upset because. . .because I've broken my engagement, but please—don't try to twist the facts. Toby had nothing to do with my decision. He knew nothing about it. I made up my mind entirely alone.'

Mrs Seaton laughed bitterly. 'Do you expect us to believe that? One minute you were ecstatically happy to be marrying Dan, the next it's all over.'

Tired to the point of no return, Liz, as bitterly, flung back, 'Ecstatically happy? I was living in a fool's paradise! Have you forgotten so soon all the broken dates, the times Dan forgot to ring me, forgot I even existed. Is that what you'd call a happy relationship? You yourself told me, Mother, that I should put my foot down.'

Aghast, Mrs Seaton said, 'I didn't mean it in that way! You didn't have to ruin the whole thing!'

'Can you ruin something that doesn't exist? Dan never loved me. You admitted as much yourself when you said he wanted to marry me so that he could get a majority holding and control the firm in fact as well as in name.'

James Seaton shot his wife a cold look. 'Why the devil did you have to tell her that?'

'I lost my temper,' she said weakly, avoiding his glance.

Elizabeth shrugged. 'Does it matter now? All these recriminations are only making matters worse. I've made up my mind.'

Her father came to her and put an arm around her shoulders, looking into her pale face with searching eyes. 'Liz, you're right. We're allowing our tempers to get out of hand. I'm sorry if I've said anything to hurt you. Toby has always been your friend, I know that. You're quite right to defend him. All I ask is that you seriously consider what you're doing.' He paused, then went on gently, 'Dan will never forgive you if you go to Italy with his cousin. You realise that? He might misunderstand your motives.'

'Dan already knows,' she said calmly. 'I've told him, and I assure you, he's perfectly well aware of my motive for going.'

He stared at her, frowning, then shrugged. 'I see.'

'Dad, I hate to defy you,' she said, then, looking appealingly into his face. 'You won't stand in my way, will you?'

Lifting his shoulders, he sighed. 'No, I suppose I won't.'

'James!' wailed his wife. 'You can't just let her

ruin her life like this. How could any girl prefer Toby to Dan? Talk to her, make her see sense.'

Liz winced at this. How, indeed, she thought, could anyone prefer another man to Dan? Her eyes were fever-bright with pain and disillusion as she turned away, and her father, watching her closely, looked satisfied.

'My dear,' he said smoothly, 'let the child do what she wants to do. It's her life. We must stand by her.'

Mrs Seaton gave him a fierce, contemptuous look. I might have known you would take that line. It's nothing to you that she's throwing away the chance of a lifetime. I wash my hands of the whole affair!'

If Elizabeth thought that she had now passed the worst of the hazards in her path, she was soon to find that she was mistaken. On the following morning, while she was eating a leisurely breakfast, Jonas descended upon her without warning.

She looked up, in surprise, as he made a predictably grand entrance, wearing his usual formal suit, leaning on a gold-headed walking stick, his sallow face grimly unsmiling.

There was a strong physical resemblance between Jonas and his grandson. She looked at him with a pang of grief, seeing Dan as he would be one day, the piercing blue eyes deep-sunk beneath dark brows, the dominating nose pinched and sharp, the fleshless cheekbones and strong jaw.

He gazed at her, brows drawn together. 'Well?

What do you mean by it, madam? Jilt my grandson, would you?'

Her chin came up instantly, her eyes defiant. 'I'm sorry! But that's my affair.'

'Little fool!' he grunted. 'Your father seems to think we should keep out of the affair.' His eyes probed her face. 'Is it true you've got involved with Toby? He's not the man for you—charming but lightweight.'

'Toby is kind, thoughtful and generous,' she protested, angered by his slighting tone.

Jonas shrugged dismissively. 'What's that to do with it? Those aren't qualities to make the pulse beat faster, damn it! And you aren't the girl to be satisfied with them, either!'

'I'm very fond of Toby,' she said lamely.

He snorted. 'Fond! What a stupid word! I'm too old a bird to be caught in your net, child. You'd soon grow tired of Toby. The fire in your hair is a tell-tale sign.' He peered at her from under the bristling brows. 'Come along, what's the truth? Quarrelled with Dan? He's a surly brute at times, I know that. Has he neglected you? We're expanding fast, you know, and Dan has many calls on his time. He can't be blamed for that. You have to realise that a busy man can't always find time for a private life.'

'I refuse to discuss it with you,' she said firmly. 'I've made up my mind—I can't marry Dan. There's nothing else to say. I'm sorry if you're disappointed, but it's our business.'

He studied her with regret. She was looking very

pretty, he thought, fresh and cool, in her dark blue dress, the green eyes reserved, but that fiery promise blazing in the silky red hair piled at the back of her head.

It had delighted him when the engagement was announced. She was perfect for Dan—a little spitfire, with enough backbone to give Dan a fight, instead of letting him walk over her at will.

Jonas was proud of his grandson. Dan had done all, and more, than he had demanded. He ran the firm like clockwork. He was clever, confident, imaginative.

And yet. . .Jonas sighed. Lacking opposition in business, Dan was fast becoming an autocrat.

It had been a shock when Dan announced that his engagement was at an end.

Jonas had stared at him, searching for a sign in Dan's controlled face of either pain or anger. The only clue to any hidden emotion had been a very slight trembling of the long fingers as Dan fixed himself a drink. Concentrating on that, Jonas had asked brutally, 'Lost her, have you? Another man, I suppose?' Dan had sipped his drink coolly, then replied that it was none of his grandfather's business.

Later, standing reflectively at his study window, the old man had heard a brief exchange between Dan and Toby which had been of considerable enlightenment.

The icy tones and wintry bleakness of Dan's face had been enough to give him away. Toby had been bright-eyed, a little impudent. Jonas, watching, had felt wrathfully inclined to kick the boy, and he rather fancied Dan had only restrained from so doing by a great effort.

He looked at Elizabeth irritably. 'Damnation, girl, I was relying on you! Dan needs you.'

'You'll have to find him another girl,' she said bitterly. 'Someone more suitable than myself.'

'What does that mean?' he asked in a sharp, watchful voice.

She shrugged. 'I'm sure you'll come up with someone who'll do for Dan!'

He laughed wryly. 'Oh, Dan won't take any interference from me! He'll find his own girls in future.'

She looked round quickly. What did he mean by that? Had it been on his advice that Dan rushed her into an engagement? Had that swift siege been only to please his grandfather?

'It might be wiser if he did,' she said quietly.

Jonas looked sharply at her, his eyes narrowed. 'Hmm. . .' he said in a thoughtful voice.

Elizabeth was very busy for the rest of that week. She gave in her notice to the library committee, who promptly sent her a young assistant who would take over when she left, and whom she found quick and efficient. Toby made all her travelling arrangements, got her work permit and after long telephone calls managed to fix up a room for her in the same apartment building as himself. He was very gay and cheerful whenever they met, and, since her family were reproachful when she was at home, she spent most of her free time in Toby's company.

On her last day in the library Aunt Kate came in to see her. She was looking very frail, Liz thought in concern, as she greeted her.

There had always been a strong resemblance between Aunt Kate and Jonas. They had the same bone structure, and the same blue eyes. But Aunt Kate had always been a gentle, loving woman, happy to devote herself to the home and family, self-effacing, soft-hearted and a little shy.

She came forward to kiss the soft, crumpled cheek, lovingly breathing in Aunt Kate's own particular scent of lavender. Aunt Kate had often been baited by Jonas because of her passion for lavender. In the summer she cut and dried the flowers from the garden, and filled tiny bags with them, hanging them in every closet, tucking them into every drawer. All her clothes carried that perfume.

'Typical old maid trick,' Jonas would snort.

Aunt Kate would blink nervously at him, then sigh. 'Mother always loved lavender, remember.'

For all her soft gentleness, she had a way of managing her brother without effort. Liz had always admired her for it.

Now Aunt Kate looked at her sadly. 'So,' she said, 'you will not be marrying Dan.' Her sigh was deep enough to make Liz feel ashamed. 'I'm very sorry, my dear, very sorry, indeed.' The faded blue eyes lifted again. 'He's taking it well, though. Dan is so good at hiding his feelings.'

A flash of pain and anger lit Elizabeth's green eyes.

Aunt Kate caught it, and looked more closely at her. 'My dear, are you sure you're doing the right thing? I was so sure you loved Dan.'

'I hate and detest him,' Elizabeth said, and was astonished to hear herself.

'I wouldn't have thought Dan would mind that,' Aunt Kate said, oddly.

Elizabeth laughed. 'No?'

Aunt Kate smiled. 'Dan isn't a man who arouses mild emotions. He would be powerless against indifference, but hate would only stimulate him.'

'Aunt Kate! The things you say!' Elizabeth laughed again.

'Ah, but I know him!' The old face was gently cunning. 'As you do, my dear! Such men are rare. They're born to command, and they need women of their own sort beside them.'

Elizabeth hesitated, then said slowly, 'Are you so sure of that?'

Her tone caught Aunt Kate's attention. Watching the girl, she asked, 'What do you mean?'

'I wonder if it's ever occurred to you that someone else might suit him better,' Elizabeth said flatly. Only to Aunt Kate could she bear even to hint at the truth. She knew that her confidence would be respected.

The blue eyes narrowed. 'Who is it, child?'

Elizabeth looked at her pleadingly. 'You swear not to breathe a word?'

'Of course, if you wish.'

Elizabeth hesitated, then said harshly, 'Karen!'

Aunt Kate stared, her jaw dropping. Then she frowned. 'Karen?'

Elizabeth waited. She could see that her suggestion had aroused a new train of thought.

Aunt Kate fumbled for a chair and sat down, staring around the small library. 'Now that you mention it,' she said, 'there has been something. . .I couldn't put my finger on it exactly. Looks between them, odd silences. I noticed without realising it.'

Elizabeth felt a fierce pang of feeling. So someone else had begun to suspect! Her own fears had not been ill-founded at all. She began instinctively to tidy a little pile of books. It helped to keep busy.

'Jonas has always wanted Dan to marry you,' Aunt Kate told her later. 'I wonder if he pushed the boy into proposing. Now he thinks you'll marry Toby.' She looked at her, waiting for her to answer, and Elizabeth smiled at her.

'Toby is a darling. I'm very fond of him.'

'But?'

'Yes,' agreed Elizabeth. 'But. . .and it's a big but. He's too much like my brother. I just used him as a smoke-screen for Dan's benefit.'

'Of course, Dan is jealous of him,' said Aunt Kate casually.

'Jealous?' Red colour ran up Elizabeth's neck and

face. Her heart shook. 'Dan, jealous?'

Aunt Kate was fingering her handbag, her head bent. 'Oh, yes, dear. He always has been—you know, Toby was such a bright, lovable child. I remember how you and he used to play together in the copse.' She chuckled. 'You used to try to frighten the life out of me! Bandits or Robin Hood—always up to some naughty trick. And Dan was jealous even then.'

'Of me?' Elizabeth asked drily. 'I was half his age, remember. A little girl! He had plenty of girlfriends, you know.'

'Oh, of course, but you'd been his pet when you were little. Don't you remember that? It was your hot temper. It amused him to see you lose it.'

'It still does, I think,' Elizabeth told her flatly.

'There's a strong streak of possessiveness in Dan. He holds to what he has, my dear, just as Jonas has always done. And he thought of you as belonging to him. When he came back from college to find Toby trailing after you all day, Dan resented it.' She laughed softly, then grimaced, bending forward.

'What is it?' Elizabeth crouched beside her, seeing her face whiten.

'Oh, a little touch of rheumatism in my chest. I've had it for a long while. It'll pass in a moment.'

'Are you sure you're well?' Elizabeth studied her anxiously. She looked so thin and frail. Her age was beginning to show.

A little irritably, Aunt Kate said, 'I'm perfectly well, my dear. Don't fuss.' She stood up. 'I must go. Enjoy yourself in Italy, Liz, but don't rush into anything, will you? You young people always think you know best, but it's the old, who are out of the game, who really see what's happening.'

Elizabeth kissed her gently. 'Thank you, dear. I'll write to you. Look after yourself.'

The night before she left for Italy, Elizabeth wandered through the copse, searching for her engagement ring. She had been looking for it ever since Dan threw it there. She could not bear to think of it lying out in the rain, rusting, the bright stone growing dull and the delicately worked metal becoming choked with earth.

It had been raining that morning. The smell of the rain was everywhere. The earth had a fresh, cool odour, and there were still shining drops of water caught on the ends of twigs, or funnelled along green cups of fern. A thrush hopped, bright-eyed, into the undergrowth at her approach, and a blackbird threw a cascade of liquid notes into the dusky sky.

She was so intent on her search that it was only when a twig cracked underfoot that she turned in surprise, and found Dan a few feet away, having approached without disturbing her.

He looked at her in the cool, veiled way which had often baffled her. Elizabeth felt a fierce surge of anger against him. What right had he had to make her love him while feeling nothing in return?

'Looking for something?' he asked.

She flushed, shaking her head. She was not going to admit to him that she had been looking for the ring he had so casually flung away.

He thrust his hands into his pockets. A silence stretched between them. He was staring up at the green laced branches, and she could safely watch him, her throat closing up with love as she traced the clear outline of nose, cheek, jaw.

Then he turned his head suddenly, and she flushed, her eyes dropping quickly away under the challenge of his.

'How is Karen?' she asked on an impulse which she at once regretted.

Dan looked surprised, then his eyes narrowed. 'She's very well,' he said slowly. 'If a little hurt.'

Her eyes shot up to his face. 'Hurt?'

'She expected you to call to say goodbye.'

'Oh.' Her mouth tightened. So Karen was hurt? She doubted it. Karen was probably too relieved and happy to care whether she saw her again or not.

Dan was watching her, his eyebrows lifted quizzically. 'No comment?'

'What do you expect me to say?'

'You might express some faint regret for having slighted one of your oldest friends,' he drawled.

'I would have called if I hadn't been busy,' she lied. 'I would have expected Karen to work that out for herself.'

'She hasn't been feeling too well,' he said curtly, 'or she would have come down to see you.'

'Is it serious?'

'No, only a touch of summer flu.' His blue eyes were icy as he stared at her through the falling dusk. 'I told her the probable reason for your neglect.'

Her heart thudded against her ribs. 'Oh?' She could hear the huskiness and uncertainty of her voice and tried to conquer it. 'What. . .what was that?'

'A desire to avoid me,' he said incisively.

Liz looked away, shrugging, then began to walk towards her own side of the copse. Dan fell into step, and she halted, looking up at him.

'There's no need to come with me,' she said coolly. 'I do know the way.'

He muttered something under his breath, going pale. She saw his mouth twitching convulsively under some sort of tension.

'Isn't some sort of farewell scene indicated?' he asked tautly.

'We have nothing to say to each other, Dan,' she said in stiff tones. 'I said my goodbye to you days ago.'

His hands shot out and caught her shoulders, making her stumble and wince at the pain of his fingers as they bit into her flesh.

'You can't just brush me off as though I were a troublesome insect,' he said brutally.

'Can't I? Just watch me!'

They glared at each other, their faces close together. A moth flitted between them, its powdery wings brushing her cheek, and she jumped and jerked her head back.

The next moment she was clamped in Dan's arms, her head bent back over his rigid arm, while he kissed her with a cruelty and burning anger which was unlike anything she had ever faced before. She struggled angrily, wrenching her head back, and he released her at once.

For a moment he looked down at her, his eyes glittering coldly and with a sardonic mockery that made her angrier than ever.

'Brush that off!' he said, then turned on his heel and stalked back through the undergrowth.

She stared after him, trembling violently. How dared he! He was a savage, after all! There had been nothing in that kiss but hatred, and now she was quite certain that he had never loved her at all. She had been a means to an end, and when she had the unexpected impudence to object to being used, he had been infuriated. That was all there was to it.

'Poor Karen,' she said aloud. Her voice sounded oddly weak and thread-like. She walked back slowly towards the house, shivering as though she had been caught in a sudden storm.

CHAPTER FOUR

EVEN in September the sun shone unfailingly at Aveni, and after two months Elizabeth was accustomed to the heat, and found it quite possible to spend her lunch hour on the beach, swimming and then eating some sandwiches before returning to the office for the afternoon. At first she had had to take a siesta in the middle of the day, but once the heat of August was over she became more and more at home in the warmer climate, and not only enjoyed her leisure more but found it easier to work.

She spent several evenings a week brushing up her rather weak Italian with a tutor whom Toby had found for her, a dark-eyed, black-haired young man whose admiration had first embarrassed, then pleased her. Her wounded pride was not proof against his constant entreaties for a date. Toby teased her about her admirer, and, flattered and amused, she responded by teasing him about the pretty secretary who found many opportunities for coming into their office with queries, fluttering her black lashes at Toby as she posed beside his desk.

After weeks of Italian sunshine, she was golden brown and full of vitality. At weekends, she and

Toby spent their days on the beach which was only a short step from the factory. It was not, admittedly, the fashionable end of the town. The tourists never came so far along the bay. But, to them, that was another of Aveni's advantages. They could sunbathe quietly under striped umbrellas, surrounded by local people who, like themselves, avoided the tourists.

The factory was a small one, like Woodhams a family firm, and Signor Perini knew every one of his employees by name. He was well liked by most of them. Short, plump and bouncy with bright black eyes, he patrolled the building during the day, keeping his eye upon the work. He had a paternal manner, clasping the men in his arms when he congratulated them on the birth of a son, a marriage or some other happy family occasion. How he always knew of these events was a mystery to Elizabeth, but he certainly did keep a finger on the pulse not only of the work, but the workers. The smallest detail of their lives interested him.

Elizabeth had liked him on sight, and he, rolling his black eyes upwards, had said, 'Ah, young lady, what trouble you will bring me! That red hair, those big eyes, your pretty legs. . . Holy Mother of God, I see fireworks ahead!'

She had blushed hotly and looked at Toby with helpless indignation.

Then Signor Perini had winked at her. 'But I forget—you are English! You will freeze when my young men lose their heads, and they will remember their manners—no?'

'Yes!' she had assured him firmly, and he had laughed with evident delight.

'Good, good.' Then he had looked at Toby. 'And you, my dear friend, you will be watchful of her?'

Toby had slid a possessive arm around her, meeting the other man's gaze directly. 'You can depend on that!' he had said.

Signor Perini had nodded slowly. 'Ah, I see! Even better! You are betrothed?'

'Not yet,' Toby had said calmly. 'But. . .' and his smile had been confident enough to make Signor Perini grin back.

'Then I need not worry! That is good. I like my little family to be happy.'

He had invited them to dinner one evening, and they had been warmly welcomed by his dark, plump wife. Elizabeth, faced with a huge plate of risotto dusted with grated Parmesan, had taken a deep breath, shuddering to think what this would do to her waist. As she ate she felt the twin dark eyes upon her, and she had smiled her enjoyment.

'You like?' the *signora* had asked eagerly.

'Very much,' Elizabeth had said with sincerity.

Signor Perini had nodded. 'My wife is very good cook. You must taste her cannelloni!'

After the meal, the *signora* took her up to see the three little boys of the house, sleeping like olive-skinned angels in their beds. Elizabeth had gently touched the smooth curved cheek of the youngest, a four-year-old, and a little sigh had broken from her

lips. Dan's sons would look just like this, she
thought, brushing back a lock of black hair from
the child's forehead.

Signora Perini had looked at her in pleased
surprise. 'You like children, yes?'

'Very much,' Elizabeth had agreed.

'You have some of your own one day,' the *signora*
had comforted, apparently reading her wistful
expression correctly.

'I hope so,' Elizabeth had smiled.

The work Elizabeth was required to do was hardly
taxing. She was mainly expected to hold the fort for
Toby when he was otherwise engaged. The new
links between Perini and Woodham were still very
new and untried. The working arrangements had to
be ironed out, the language problems involved were
complicated and Elizabeth was grateful that, under
her tutor's guidance, she was gradually becoming
easier in the language.

Her affection for Toby was strengthened by
seeing him under stress conditions several times.
He coped admirably with the emotional Latin
temperament, soothing, calming, explaining and
never losing his own temper. His cheerfulness, she
realised, was only a surface reflection. Underneath
he was, as her father had said, an ambitious and
clever young man. Dan had chosen well in sending
him on this particular job. Toby handled it perfectly.

'What are you doing tomorrow night?' he asked

her one clear September afternoon.

'I have a date,' she smiled.

'With your tutor?'

'Yes—with Antonio. He's taking me to the new restaurant. They have a new trio there—he says they're very good.'

'Pop group?'

'Italian-style,' she agreed. 'Rather more musical than pop, I fancy, but they sing popular Italian songs.'

Toby looked at her thoughtfully. 'I don't want to play the heavy father. I know I let Perini think we were almost engaged, but I did that for your own protection. You won't let this Antonio get serious, will you?'

She smiled at him. 'I'm not a child, Toby. Of course I won't.'

'Well, you know what Italians are like—very hot-blooded and so on!'

'They don't use strong-arm tactics, you know,' she said, with some amusement. 'Very romantic and ardent, but perfect manners.'

He flipped an eyebrow quizzically. 'You speak from your own experience?'

'Yes,' she said firmly.

'Well, so long as you know what you're doing! Am I still allowed to make dates with you, or do you prefer Italians now?'

Elizabeth looked quickly at him, suspecting a little touch of resentment in his tone.

'Don't be silly! Of course I'd love a date!'

He grinned, the sulky look vanishing. 'That's a relief. When?'

'I'm free on Wednesday,' she said. 'Antonio gives me a lesson the day after our date.'

'I only hope his lessons are linguistic,' he said lightly.

She wrinkled up her nose. 'They are, don't worry! He takes his job very seriously and is very good at it.'

On the following evening, she was putting away her work when the door opened behind her and, looking round, she was stunned to see Dan standing in the room.

The colour rushed out of her face, then flooded back again. She straightened up abruptly.

'Where's Toby?' he asked as coolly as though they were mere acquaintances.

'He's with Signor Perini,' she said, summoning all her self-control in order to stop her voice from shaking.

He strolled forward and looked around the room with calm interest.

'How are things going? Toby sends me a report every week, but I thought I should see for myself.'

'I think everything is working out very well,' she said, resuming the job of clearing her desk.

'Good.' He turned and studied her with narrowed eyes which brought an angry flush to her cheeks. 'You're very brown. Do you get down to the beach much?'

'Quite often,' she said curtly.

'I've never seen you with such a strong tan. I rather thought your skin didn't take to the sun.'

'I took it easily at first,' she said. 'Gradually I suppose one becomes acclimatised.'

He nodded. 'How do you get on with the other workers? Good relations?'

'Very,' she said, picking up her bag and standing poised for departure.

'There's no resentment? Because you're a foreigner?'

'None at all, so far as I know. Rather the opposite, I should say. I've found the men very friendly.'

His glance was deliberate and sardonic. 'I believe you.'

Elizabeth flushed as those hard blue eyes ran over her, and turned to the door to go.

'I'll find Toby and tell him you're here. He wasn't expecting you, was he?'

'No,' he said, joining her. 'I wanted to surprise him.'

She looked at him over her shoulder. 'I think you will.' And me, she thought. I've been knocked off balance by his sudden appearance. Was that, too, intended? Why has he come? She looked at him calmly, trying hard to keep her expression noncommittal.

'If you'll wait here, I'll find Toby, then.'

'Are you going home now?' Dan asked quickly. 'I thought we might have dinner together.'

She stiffened. 'Thank you, but I already have an

appointment.' How dared he invite her to dinner in that easy tone, as though they were casually met strangers! He had the impudence of the devil! Then a thought occurred to her, and she looked at him with sudden sharpness. Was it possible that he had come here to announce his engagement to Karen, to tell Toby?

'Is there any news from home?' she asked lightly, watching him.

His eyes were unrevealing. 'I was going to tell you all that over dinner. Why don't you change your mind? Is your appointment urgent? Could it be cancelled?'

The door opened and Antonio stood there, very elegant in a lightweight blue suit and crisp white shirt, his bronzed skin glowing with health, the liquid black eyes eager.

'Elizabeth,' he said, in his smooth Latin voice, 'I was wondering where you had hidden yourself! I have been waiting for you, darling.'

She flushed, feeling Dan's cold sardonic gaze upon her profile. Smiling at Antonio, she said, 'I'm so sorry—I'm coming right away, but first I must find Toby.'

'Here I am,' Toby said curtly, from behind Antonio.

'Oh, Toby—' Elizabeth began, stammering slightly, then stopped as she saw his face.

He was looking furious, his brown eyes hard and cold. 'Liz,' he began sharply, 'what is all this?' Then he stopped, staring past her at Dan. 'Good

God, what are you doing here?' he demanded.

Dan's mouth twitched slightly, as though he was amused. 'I flew over to check up on our investment,' he said coolly.

Antonio looked from one to the other of them, then made a courteous gesture. 'Perhaps it is better if I wait in the car, Elizabeth? You will not be too long?'

'No,' she promised. 'I'm sorry, Tonio. I'll hurry.'

When he had slipped away, Toby took his narrowed gaze from Dan and looked at her. 'May I have a private word before you dash off?' His voice was unusually hard, and she looked at him in puzzled alarm.

'Of course.'

He waved her through the door into the bare corridor outside, glancing back at Dan, unsmilingly. 'I won't keep you long, Dan.'

Dan lifted his shoulders in a shrug.

When the door had closed on him, Toby turned on her angrily. 'Liz, we're in trouble. You made a mistake in translation, and a whole batch of transistors were wrongly labelled. Perini is hopping mad. He blames me, of course—it's my department.'

'Oh, I'm sorry, Toby,' she said, horrified. 'I'll go to him and explain that it was my fault.'

'Don't be damned ridiculous! I'm not a little boy—I don't need to shield myself behind you. Just make sure it doesn't happen again. I don't like being carpeted for a mistake I didn't make.'

She put her hand on his arm and looked anxiously at him. 'Toby, I really am sorry. Perhaps I ought to resign. My Italian really isn't very good, you know.'

'Don't be an idiot,' he said, then relented and smiled at her. 'I'll forgive you this time. I'm sorry, too—I got hot under the collar. I shouldn't have blamed you. I made you come, and I'm glad I did.'

She kissed his cheek impulsively, and his arms came round her and held her close. She looked up, surprised, and found his brown eyes very near her own. There was a tenderness in them that astonished her.

'Dear Liz,' he said softly. 'Thank you for being so forgiving. I was a beast to you just now.' He grinned. 'Do you think I could be jealous of your hot-blooded Latin lover?'

She leaned against him, comforted by his affection. 'Idiot, Toby,' she said teasingly.

His eyes crinkled in amusement. 'No? Are you sure?'

'Quite sure,' she said firmly.

He bent his head and kissed her lightly on the mouth. She was too surprised to respond or withdraw, standing there passive under the touch of his lips.

The door opened and Toby looked over her head. His tone was gay and slightly insolent. 'Sorry, Dan—tired of waiting? I think we've sorted out our little problem now.' He released her, smiling down at her. 'Run along then, honey. See you tomorrow.'

She nodded and turned, avoiding Dan's eyes. She heard Toby say brightly, 'Now then, Dan, this is a surprise! Checking up on me, are you?'

The restaurant was crowded, but the food was superb and the music warmly romantic. They sat at a small table on the pavement, sipping the local wine and talking in soft voices while the music throbbed plaintively in the background.

'You look very beautiful, tonight,' Tonio said, gazing at Elizabeth over the rim of his glass.

She smiled at him absently. Her thoughts were in such turmoil that she found it hard to be ordinarily polite. Dan's sudden arrival had been too much of a shock. She could not help wondering exactly why he had come—and what news he brought. He had seemed different, somehow—calmer, more remote, as though he had accepted their broken engagement now. Was he, after all, relieved that now he could marry Karen, even though it meant the abandonment of his cherished plans for the control of the company?

Tonio put down his glass and leaned across the table, his hand reaching for hers.

She blinked at him, snapping out of her abstraction.

'Darling, Elizabeth,' he said, his voice delightfully accented. 'Do you mind that I call you darling? It is so pretty. My English is very good. I like England. I live in London for a year.'

'Yes, I know,' she said, allowing her hand to lie limply in his grasp. 'You told me.'

His liquid eyes caressed her face. 'English voices are so slow and cool. I like to hear you speak. Is something wrong? You seem very silent tonight. Usually you talk much to me. Have I offended you?'

She shook her head. 'Of course not! I was thinking about my work, actually.' It was a lie, but she could hardly tell him the truth.

He shrugged generously. 'Oh, work! Too dull on such a night.'

She looked round, smiling. 'Yes, it is a lovely night, isn't it?'

The sky was a warm, glowing purple. The air lay cool as wine on her arms and shoulders, refreshing after the heat of the day.

'You like to dance?' he asked her. 'We dance now, and have our coffee later?'

There was a space cleared in the centre of the restaurant, and a few couples were dancing dreamily. Liz looked across the pavement at them and hesitated, then shrugged.

'Why not?'

They rose and moved into the well-lit room. Tonio's hand rested proudly on her shoulder, his head bent attentively towards her. A mirror hung behind the bar at the other side of the room. She vaguely glimpsed herself and Tonio in its shining surface. She was unfamiliar to herself, her skin glowing and tanned, her simple white dress flaring at the hem as she walked. Then her eyes widened in shock as she caught a fleeting glimpse of a familiar dark head in the mirror. Dan! What on earth was he doing here, of all places? She watched his reflection bitterly. He bent forward to light a cigarette, and she saw that he was with Toby, who leant towards him to offer a light. So Toby had brought Dan here! He had known perfectly well that she was going to be here tonight. Why had Toby done it?

Tonio's arm slid down her back slowly and tightened round her waist.

She turned towards him, smiling up into his face.

The music swirled round them. Tonio's white teeth gleamed against his brown skin. 'Ah, you dance so beautifully! I, too, am a good dancer.'

And modest with it, she thought in amusement. He caught the fleeting smile in her lifted eyes, and smiled back, pleased with himself.

'You agree?'

'Yes,' she said honestly. 'You dance quite beautifully.' He had a graceful lope, she thought, like a rather charming wolf, as he swung her around the small floor.

When the music ended they walked back towards their table. Toby rose and waved. Tonio paused, frowning for a second, then he smiled back and looked down at her.

'Ah, your friends! You wish to speak with them?' His eyes pleaded with her.

'No,' she said. 'I see enough of them at work.'

Toby apparently read their expressions, for he

pushed back his chair and walked over to them, his usually charming face set.

'Liz, you must come and say a few words to Dan.' He looked at Tonio without smiling. 'Sorry to interrupt, but it is a family matter.'

Tonio spread his hands reluctantly. 'Oh, family! I understand, of course. Family business is important.'

He hesitated, as though wondering whether he was expected to join them. Toby made up his mind for him by giving him a nod and saying, 'Liz will join you again later. Why not have a drink while you're waiting?' Then, before Tonio could reply, he took her arm and marched her over to Dan.

Under her breath she muttered, 'What are you doing, Toby? You have got a nerve!'

'Sorry, love, but I was telling the truth. Dan has some bad news.'

Her heart thudded. 'Bad?' Would Toby describe his sister's engagement to Dan as bad news? she wondered wryly. Or was there something else?

Dan stood up as she joined them. Toby pushed her into a chair, sat down himself. She looked across the table at Dan with as much assurance as she could muster.

'What is this news?' she asked coolly.

Dan shot Toby a glance. 'You haven't told her?'

'No time,' Toby said succinctly.

Dan turned back to her, his hard face oddly gentle. 'Liz, it's Aunt Kate. . .'

She broke in anxiously. 'I knew it! She looked so frail the last time I saw her! She's ill?'

He nodded. 'I'm afraid so. It. . .it's hopeless—incurable. She's been ill for months, but she would never admit it. Now she's had to face the facts, but she still thinks she'll get better.' His face contorted in a grimace of pain and anger. 'She won't, of course, but I'm not going to be the one to tell her that.' He looked at her grimly. 'You and Toby must come home. You'll want to see her. But she knows that Toby is out here for a year, so she'll suspect something if he comes home suddenly. We have to concoct a reason for you both to fly home.'

'A holiday?' she suggested.

He looked at Toby. 'Too thin,' he said. 'She'd see through it.'

'We talked it over,' Toby added, sliding an arm round her shoulders. 'Liz, if you and I got engaged we would go home to spread the good news, wouldn't we?'

She sat upright, her face flooding with angry colour. 'So you talked it over?' she gasped. 'Nice of you! Am I being consulted, or is it all decided for me?'

Dan lit another cigarette. Through the smoke his eyes narrowed on her. 'You have a choice,' he said sardonically. 'Toby—or me? Aunt Kate is a romantic. She would cheerfully believe that I followed you out here with the hope of persuading you to change your mind and marry me after all.'

She glared at him, her green eyes shooting sparks of hostility. 'Pretend to be engaged to you again? I'd rather die!'

His dark brows lifted quizzically. 'Melodramatic, but I get your point. Then it's Toby.' His lips twitched. 'I rather thought it might be.' The blue eyes mocked her. 'And who knows, you might find you like being engaged to him?'

Toby flushed. 'Thanks. There's no need to sound so doubtful about that.'

Dan didn't even glance in his direction. His eyes fixed Elizabeth's, their expression challenging.

Slowly, she said, 'I think the whole idea is ridiculous. Why not just take us home without playing out this silly charade? Tell Aunt Kate we were homesick, or bad at our jobs, or anything?'

'Aunt Kate isn't a fool,' Dan said. 'What she needs most at the moment is reassurance, comfort.' His eyes had become scornful and there was ice in his voice. 'Do you grudge her that last service? Is your pathetic pride more important to you than her happiness?'

Elizabeth raised her chin, stung by the contempt in his tone. 'Oh, very well! I'll play your silly game!' She gave him a long, cold look. 'But only for Aunt Kate's sake.'

He relaxed, smiling ironically. 'Of course—what else?'

'I don't like being manipulated, Dan,' she said. 'I know how your Machiavellian mind works. I don't trust you.'

His eyes mocked her again, the tiny muscles at the corners of his mouth twitched in amusement. 'Don't you, Liz?'

The slow, lazy warmth in his voice made her feel weak and dizzy. He had never used that intimate, teasing voice to her lately. When she was young he had often teased her, amused to see her fly into a temper.

Toby moved restlessly, staring from one to the other of them. 'Well, it's settled, is it?' he asked a little crossly.

She turned her head, startled to remember that he was there. 'Yes,' she stammered. 'Yes, it is.'

He grinned, his eyes dancing. 'Well, well, well, so we're engaged!' He leant forward and kissed her briefly on the mouth. 'I shall enjoy this!'

CHAPTER FIVE

SIGNOR Perini was charmingly concerned when he heard their news.

'Your aunt? Oh, how sad! Yes, of course you must go! These family occasions are more important than business.' He kissed Elizabeth's hand with a flourish. 'And we shall look forward to seeing you back with us again. We have grown used to seeing our pretty English girl around, eh? My workers will be lonely without a sight of that red head every morning.' His black eyes twinkled and he grinned at Dan, standing watchfully in the background. 'She is very popular, you see!'

'I can imagine,' Dan drawled.

Elizabeth gave him a brief, cold look. The note of sarcasm was not lost on her, even if Signor Perini chose to take Dan's remark as a jovial agreement.

Toby was busy in the office, dealing with as much paperwork as he could before leaving, so Dan offered to drive her back to the building in which she and Toby had rooms.

Dan had already booked their flights home. He was staying overnight in a luxury hotel near the sea front. They were to leave for the airport early next

85

day, and Elizabeth had to pack her belongings that evening.

'Will you have dinner with me?' Dan asked her as he negotiated the corner in his hired car.

'No,' she said bluntly. 'I have too much to do.'

He pulled up outside the building. She turned to open the door. Dan leaned across and flipped up the handle. His arm lay heavily across her, barring her exit.

'Is there some reason why we should be enemies?' he asked her coolly. 'I should have said I was the one with a grievance, but you act as though I'd done you some terrible injury. I've often heard it said that people can never forgive those they've hurt, even when they're sweetly forgiving to anyone who hurts them. I suppose it applies to women.'

She looked icily at him through her lashes. 'I don't think we ever had much to say to each other, Dan. Under the spell of infatuation, I may have thought so once—I know better now.'

He laughed in an irritating fashion. 'Under the spell of infatuation? You're talking like a Victorian melodrama.'

'And you act like one,' she said furiously, pushing at his impeding arm. 'May I get out now?'

He dropped his arm and she hurriedly climbed out, slamming the door behind her. As she ran up the steps she heard the engine start up and saw, out of the corner of her eye, the sleek lines of the car gliding away.

She packed up her things and left them with the

manager of the building to be stored while she was away. She was taking a few clothes back home, and some souvenirs which she had bought for the family; glass animals for her mother, who collected them, a silk scarf for her father and a dashing ski sweater for Tom. She had dashed out that morning to buy these, and had also bought a fragile white lace shawl for Aunt Kate.

She sat on her bed, fingering it, wistfully wondering how long Aunt Kate would be there to wear it. It seemed somehow impossible to imagine a world in which Aunt Kate was not around to admire, comfort, chuckle at her jokes. The two families had almost seemed like one to her, when she was small, since they were so often together. When Dan was not at her house she had been at his, and Aunt Kate had always been there in the background, gently watching them as they played.

Elizabeth shivered as she packed the shawl away in a bed of fine tissue. Why did people get old? She felt as though someone was walking over her own grave. A coldness invaded her, and she went to stand by the window, gazing out at the calm Italian sky.

The flight was comfortable, but towards the end they ran into an electric storm, and Elizabeth tensed, seeing the flash of lightning so close.

She was sitting beside Toby. He had fallen asleep soon after they took off. He had worked very late the previous night, and looked drained and pale when he joined her in Dan's car. She glanced at him, hoping he would wake up, but his face had the blankness of sleep, and he did not move. She gripped the arms of her seat, clenching her teeth in order to fight down the panic which was threatening her. I will not be frightened, she told herself firmly, but it was just whistling in the dark. Storms had always terrified her.

Then Dan leaned forward and looked at her hard. He was seated on the other side of Toby, and had been reading a magazine since take-off. His brows signalled a query and his lips formed the words, 'Are you all right?'

Liz tried to smile, but her mouth quivered, involuntarily. 'Yes,' she mouthed back.

He reached a hand across Toby's unconscious form. She looked at it for a second, then put her own hand into the long brown fingers with a grateful sigh. Dan squeezed her hand gently, then his grip relaxed and she sat back a little, closing her eyes. The human contact made it easier to bear the storm which was raging outside the windows.

She had always hated flying, and particularly hated it in stormy weather. Her stomach was churning round like a washing machine, and her skin was cold and clammy.

As suddenly as they had flown into the storm, they flew out of it, and she gently withdrew her hand from Dan's grasp, smiling her thanks at him across Toby.

He nodded and returned to his magazine. She glanced around and saw a girl in a neighbouring seat eyeing Dan with obvious interest and approval.

Something in that open appraisal made Elizabeth look back at him, too. It was not surprising, she thought, that a stranger should so clearly find him attractive. He was that sort of man—lean, self-assured, ruggedly good-looking.

He looked up and caught her eye. For a few seconds they stared at each other, their glance direct and expressionless. Then Elizabeth looked away, flushing.

She had known Dan all her life, and he was a complete stranger, she thought as she stared out of the window. What did he think behind that baffling mask? What sort of man was he, really?

She realised that she had been confused, when they met again on her return from London, and had mistaken the adult man whom she then met for an older version of the boy who had teased, brow-beaten, managed her as a child. But people did change. The child might be father to the man, but there was a great difference between the two. The whole of a life experience had separated the boy Dan from the man whom she had met again and fell in love with so wildly.

Aunt Kate lay back against her pillows, so small and white and frail that Elizabeth felt a giant hand clutch at her heart in pity and grief. But there was the same sweetness and concern in the faded blue eyes as she kissed Elizabeth's cheek.

'Engaged to Toby! So soon!' Then, flushing slightly, Aunt Kate stammered, 'Oh, I'm not criticising you, my dear. Young people must go their own way. But I had so hoped that. . .' she broke off sighing. 'Well, there we are! It's your life, after all.'

Elizabeth looked at her lovingly. 'I brought you a present, dear.'

'A present!' Aunt Kate looked enchanted. 'That was very kind of you, Liz!' She took the tissue-wrapped parcel and gazed at it with bright eyes. 'What can it be?' She squeezed it gently and then began slowly to unwrap the tissue folds, carefully rolling up the blue silk ribbon Elizabeth had used to tie it.

Elizabeth sat down on the edge of the bed and watched her with sad eyes.

'Oh!' With a soft, breathed sigh Aunt Kate shook out the cobwebby folds and smoothed the lace with her wrinkled hand. 'Oh, it's lovely! I shall be as grand as a queen in this, shan't I?'

Elizabeth helped her to drape it softly around her thin shoulders. Then she fetched a hand mirror and Aunt Kate studied herself with eager eyes.

'You can hold court this afternoon,' Liz said, patting her hand. 'Toby wants to come up and see you for tea.'

'You must both come,' Aunt Kate nodded. 'That will be nice. I shall enjoy that.' She lay back with a sigh of relief, as though it tired her just to sit up for a moment.

'Do you want to sleep?' asked Elizabeth. 'Shall I go?'

'No, dear, stay and talk to me. I get bored up here on my own. Alice is very busy, you know. This house is really too big. Karen is very good, but she has her own work.' Aunt Kate settled herself more easily. 'My mother had some beautiful shawls, when I was young. They came from India, you know—silk, with long fringes, and such colours! One was black with scarlet and green peacocks embroidered on it. I used to gaze at it with such envy!'

Elizabeth smiled. 'Women wore lovely clothes in the Victorian and Edwardian eras, didn't they?'

'Oh, so beautiful, my dear! You can't imagine! But although they looked so nice, they were very cumbersome, you know, and restricted people's movements.'

'One always imagines women strolling in a leisurely way, with parasols over their heads and long white gloves. . .' said Elizabeth wistfully.

'Those parasols! Now that was a delightful fashion! I wonder that they've never been brought back. Mother had a Japanese one, made of waxed silk, with a dragon coiled all round it. When she walked in the sun one could see the dragon shimmering through the fineness of the silk—just as if it was alive and moving.' Aunt Kate's eyes were vaguely fixed on the window and her face had a dreamy expression.

She went on talking about the past for a while, her voice growing more and more sleepy, and at last she stopped talking and lay very still, her lids drooping.

Elizabeth lightly drew the covers up around her shoulders, then tiptoed out of the room and closed the door very gently. When she came down into the sitting-room, she found Dan and Jonas sitting there, staring at each other in a grim sort of silence.

Jonas peered at her from under his bristling brows. 'Oh, it's you, Liz! Well, girl, how is she?'

'Very weak,' she said sadly.

'I know that!' he said in an irritated tone. 'How is she in herself, I meant! Is she cheerful?'

'She seems to be very cheerful,' Liz agreed. 'She was talking about the past most of the time.'

'What's cheerful about that?' he barked. 'Kate was always a sentimental old fool.' He stood up with some difficulty, breathing hard as he straightened his shoulders, leaning on his stick. 'Well, I'm going for a stroll around the garden. Must keep healthy. No point in falling sick myself, is there?'

Dan stood up. 'Shall I walk with you, sir?'

Jonas turned on him angrily. 'No, damn you! I'm not senile yet! I don't need a nurse.' He glared at Elizabeth. 'Talk some sense into this silly little girl. If she marries that pea-brained Toby she'll regret it!'

Elizabeth stiffened but did not retort. For all his brusque manners she could see that his sister's illness had upset him badly.

When he had stumped out of the room, Dan gestured to a chair. 'Toby is down at the factory this morning,' he said. 'He'll be back for lunch. You'd better stay.'

'Aunt Kate looks very fragile,' she said, sinking into the chair.

He nodded. 'Yes.'

'I think she accepted our story about the engagement,' she told him, after a silence. 'At first she was suspicious, but she was only worried about you, it seems. She had some notion that you'd flown to Italy for my sake.'

'I know,' he said curtly.

Elizabeth looked at him. 'Are you sure she believes she will get well? She seems to be living in the past, as though she'd already relinquished the present.'

'She's very frightened of dying,' he said. 'She told me that once—when she broke her leg a few years back. She was in a state of shocking panic. I sat up with her all night. I wouldn't like to see her like that again.'

'No,' Liz agreed. 'She's so gentle and kind. I've always been very fond of her.'

'She took my mother's place for me,' he said roughly. 'I owe her more than I could ever repay. She made my childhood much happier than it might have been. Jonas was very good to me, of course, but he had no idea how to treat a child. He bullied and threatened most of the time. It was lucky for me that I had Aunt Kate in the background.'

She looked at him thoughtfully. It must have been pretty grim for him, she realised, being left without parents at so early an age. She had not known him then. She had only come into his life

when he was in his teens. He had been ten years old
when she was born. Her first memory of him dated
from her third birthday. She had thrown a piece of
birthday cake at him and he had made faces at her,
half amused, half indulgent.

How did he remember her? she wondered. It had
been an odd relationship, really, that close link
between a teenage boy and a very small girl. He had
been friend, protector, enemy rolled into one—
always at hand when she needed help, always
available for playing games. Under his sometimes
teasing manner there had been a hidden streak of
chivalry which rose to the surface whenever she was
in trouble. All that had ended at some time. When?
she asked herself. When he went away to university? Or when Toby arrived on the scene, so much
nearer her own age and on the spot while Dan was
far away?

Lunch was a silent meal. Jonas was in one of his
grim moods, his brows permanently drawn
together. Dan was equally withdrawn, and only
Aunt Alice seemed her normal self.

She was very well preserved for her age, her
brown hair slightly tinged with silver here and
there, but her complexion still clear and smooth.
Her brown eyes were as warm as her son's, but
lacked that glint of mischief which made Toby so
appealing.

She treated Elizabeth very much as she had
always done, smiling at her as she passed the salad
bowl, her glance gently approving.

Elizabeth knew that Toby was the apple of his mother's eye. Anyone who loved Toby would be welcome to Alice Harries, and of course, she could not know that the engagement was a mere trick to deceive Aunt Kate and give her a brief peace of mind.

Elizabeth helped her to wash up after lunch. The kitchen was bright and well planned. Dan had insisted on having it modernised only a few years ago, and the uniform surfaces and gay yellow paint made it both charming and sensible.

'This is the nicest kitchen I've ever seen,' she told Aunt Alice as she deftly set the plates to drain.

'Dan designed it all himself,' Aunt Alice nodded. 'So kind and clever of him. He made me work in here for half an hour while he watched me, so that he could work out the most functional design. The heights are all perfect.' She smiled around the room. 'And of course, the colour scheme is so soothing on a grey rainy morning. One feels happy working in here—it gives the illusion of sunshine whatever the weather.'

'Dan is very capable,' Elizabeth said, a trifle drily.

Aunt Alice looked at her in surprise, and Elizabeth flushed. She had not meant to sound quite so tart.

'My dear,' said Aunt Alice doubtfully, 'you are sure about Toby, aren't you?' Her cheeks grew rather pink and she looked at Elizabeth uncertainly, a little apologetically. 'I mean, it's so soon after. . .well, I really don't mean to sound critical. I would be very happy to see you and Toby married. But. . .'

'After Dan?' Elizabeth met her eyes frankly. 'I understand your doubts. I can promise you one thing—that I won't marry Toby unless I'm absolutely certain I love him.'

Aunt Alice sighed. 'And you're not yet sure?'

Elizabeth hesitated. This pretended engagement was proving even more embarrassing than she had expected. Dan had forgotten, when he and Toby hatched up their little plot, that Aunt Kate was not the only person in the world to be affected by the story. Nothing happened in a vacuum.

'I'm not sure yet,' she said, after a long moment.

'Does Toby realise that?' Aunt Alice sounded sharp, half annoyed.

Elizabeth nodded. 'Oh, yes, he understands.'

'Well, that's more than I do,' Aunt Alice said, slamming the cupboard door.

Elizabeth looked at her regretfully. 'I'm sorry. I realise how it sounds. . .'

'Young people never cease to baffle me,' said Aunt Alice. 'I know there's no point in asking for explanations. I wouldn't get the real truth, either from you or Toby. It all seems so very wrong to me.'

Elizabeth sighed. 'I'm sorry.'

With Toby later, she tried to explain her feeling of uneasiness. 'Your mother now thinks me completely unreliable. I felt quite sick.'

'Oh, she'll come round,' he said easily. 'Stop

looking so miserable, green eyes.' His dancing smile shone at her. 'The main thing is, Aunt Kate believed it. She asked me this afternoon if we would be staying in England long. Were we going to have an engagement party? She seems quite keen on that idea—said we could have it when she was up out of bed again.'

'Oh, no,' groaned Elizabeth in anguish. 'Poor darling!'

Toby slid an arm round her. 'Don't cry, darling. She seemed so happy. If you ask me, we're worrying more than she is!'

'Because she thinks she's going to get better,' Elizabeth pointed out.

His face sobered. 'Yes, I suppose so. And of course, we can't stay for long, in fact. We have to get back to Italy in a week or so. If we didn't go back, it would certainly arouse her suspicions.' He looked at her searchingly. 'We may have to keep up our pretence for quite a while, you realise.'

'Dan thinks it won't be long,' she sighed. 'The doctors think a matter of a few weeks.'

They were silent for a while. Karen came slowly round the corner of the house and Elizabeth, looking up, caught sight of a white misery in the other girl's face which vanished as soon as she saw them.

Smiling brightly, far too brightly, Karen came forward and said, 'Hello, Liz! Nice to see you again.'

Elizabeth smiled back. 'How are you?'

'Oh, I'm fine!' Karen's voice was a little too high,

but she met Elizabeth's eyes directly and without any hint of the feelings Elizabeth knew must lie beneath the surface.

Baffled and angry, Elizabeth wondered what on earth Dan was playing at to leave Karen suspended like this when he was now free to marry her if he chose.

If he chose! Was that the problem? Did Dan not choose to marry his cousin because she was of no possible use to him in his career? Karen would not bring him much money. She had not inherited a large block of shares in Woodhams, and she had little to offer but love.

Contempt burned in her chest. How despicable he was, and how he had fooled her once!

She looked sharply at Karen, seeing the telltale shadows under her eyes, the new hollows in her cheeks. Surely, she thought, Karen had lost a great deal of weight! She looked quite unlike the plump and smiling girl whom she had last seen with Dan. Her hands were slender and delicate, her waist very slim. Despite her look of weary misery, Karen had a new prettiness. Her slim figure gave her far more of an impact.

'How is Tom?' Karen suddenly asked her.

Elizabeth blinked. 'Oh, he's very well.' She glanced at the other girl curiously. 'Haven't you seen him at the factory?'

Karen flushed. 'No,' she said briefly.

Elizabeth was puzzled for a moment, then she understood. Of course, Karen was too guilty to visit the family of a girl whom she had cut out. Poor Karen! Her secret love for Dan had done her a great deal of harm. It was obviously weighing on her mind, making her nervous and unhappy. How could Dan let it happen?

Toby strolled away to admire a clump of chrysanthemums, their rust and bronze colours blending delightfully in the border.

Karen looked sideways at Elizabeth. 'Liz, I. . .there's something I've often wanted to tell you, but I just couldn't bear to, somehow.'

Elizabeth's throat tightened. This was it! At last Karen was going to admit the truth, bring it all out into the open. She felt a fierce pang, then a sickening feeling of relief. Anything was better than not being certain. This slow torture of suspicion and distrust was emotionally crippling.

'Yes, Karen?' she asked gently, nodding at her in an encouraging way.

Karen was visibly trembling, her fingers shaking so much that she had to wind them together in her lap.

'I. . .it's a personal problem, you see, and I wasn't too sure how you would react.' She looked up briefly, her glance flying to Elizabeth's attentive face and then away again. 'You're so sure of yourself, so clever and confident. You and Dan. . .' her voice broke then, and for a moment she sat, her head bent, saying nothing.

Elizabeth put a hand on her arm. 'Go on,' she urged. 'Dan and I?'

'You. . .you were so alike, so good at managing your lives.' Karen smiled wanly. 'Whereas I'm shy and rather stupid. I even managed to make a mess out of falling in love. . .' She broke off again, biting her lip. Then she said rapidly, breathlessly, 'That's it, you see. I mean, that's what I wanted you to know. When you broke off your engagement to Dan you couldn't know what it meant to me. . . I'm sorry, of course, that it happened for you. I wasn't being selfishly gloating, Liz, but if you knew what a relief it was!'

Calmly, Elizabeth said, 'Yes, Karen?'

The other girl laughed in a brittle, angry fashion. 'It sounds so selfish, the way I'm putting it, and really, I was very sad for you. But it made me feel less inadequate, too, you see. If even you could make a mistake, then I needn't feel so useless.' She looked appealingly at Elizabeth. 'Am I sounding terribly hard and self-centred?'

'Of course not,' Elizabeth soothed. 'Just human! You were wrong about me, anyway. I think we always tend to think that other people are more efficient and well adjusted than we are—we can't see beneath the surface they show us. They put on an act and we believe it.'

'Was it an act?' Karen looked searchingly, hopefully at her. 'Was your air of confidence just an act, Liz?'

'Most of the time!'

'I can't believe you're as riddled with self-doubt as I am, though.' Karen's eyes were wistful. 'Being fat makes you very uncertain of yourself.'

'You certainly are not fat now,' Elizabeth said, laughing. 'You look very slim and elegant. I was just noticing that a few moments ago. Have you been dieting?'

Karen shook her head. 'No.' She looked down at her figure with an air of surprised appraisal. 'I am much slimmer, though.'

Elizabeth watched her for a moment, then she said lightly, 'And are you going to tell me about him?'

Karen flushed hotly. 'Him?' she parried.

Elizabeth looked a little wryly at her. 'The man you're in love with, of course.'

Behind them they heard Dan's voice raised as he spoke to Toby. He had walked out of the house without either of them noticing him.

Karen shot him a nervous look. 'Oh, no,' she said quickly to Elizabeth. 'I. . .I couldn't. . .not to you!'

'Why not?' Elizabeth asked her coolly. 'I thought that that was what you intended to do? You were going to tell me about him, weren't you?'

Karen bit her lip. 'I forgot that. . .Anyway, it was a silly idea. You're the last person I can talk to!' Then she jumped up and ran into the house without another word.

CHAPTER SIX

'WHY DOES Kate keep harping on this idea of an engagement party?' Jonas said irritably. 'Anyone would imagine it was she who was planning to get married!'

'She has got a bee in her bonnet about it,' Elizabeth agreed, sighing. 'But if it will make her happy I suppose we could do something on those lines. . .'

'No,' said Dan curtly. 'It's out of the question. We don't want the news of this engagement to go beyond the family.'

Jonas stared at him quizzically, the thick brows meeting over his strong, autocratic nose. 'Hmm. . .why is that?'

'Yes,' said Toby, coming into the room and dropping down on the arm of Elizabeth's chair with a grin, 'why?'

Dan met Toby's mischievous, dancing eyes with a cool stare. His voice was hostile.

'You know perfectly well why!'

'I do not,' said Jonas. 'Tell me!'

There was a silence. Elizabeth, her face pale and angry, erupted. 'Because,' she snapped, 'the whole thing is phoney!'

Jonas chuckled. 'Good gracious me! Do you say so?'

She looked at him searchingly. His eyes twinkled. 'You knew!' she accused.

'I suspected,' Jonas agreed, inclining his head. 'There was a whiff of stage-management about the affair. Dan suddenly flying off to Italy and returning with the pair of you, and a cock-and-bull story about an engagement!'

'You won't tell Aunt Kate, will you?' she asked in alarm.

Jonas looked offended. 'Certainly not! What purpose lies behind it, though?' And he glanced at Dan.

'I had to bring them back,' Dan explained. 'I couldn't let Aunt Kate die without seeing them again, but if they'd rushed back so soon, she would have known that her illness was much worse than she imagines.'

'You shouldn't have sent Toby to Italy in the first place,' Jonas told him unbendingly.

'I didn't realise, when I made those arrangements, that Aunt Kate was quite so ill. By the time I was aware of it, it was too late to change the plan.' His voice halted abruptly, and he frowned, as though biting back something.

'What on earth made you dream up a mock engagement?' Jonas demanded scathingly.

Dan looked sideways at Elizabeth, a derisive smile on his firm mouth. 'It seemed like a good idea at the time. It has at least given Aunt Kate something else to think about, taken her mind off darker subjects.'

'We all have to die,' Jonas said. 'Kate must face that. It's no good running away from the truth.'

'How can you be so callous?' Elizabeth flared. 'Because you're strong enough to bear the truth it doesn't give you the right to criticise her. Some people are more vulnerable than others, and often that makes them more human. Strong people are not exactly lovable.'

Jonas looked highly amused. 'Is that a shaft aimed at me, or Dan?'

She flushed, aware that she had said more than she intended. 'It was just a generalisation, but if the cap fits. . .'

Toby laughed. 'You asked for that, Jonas!'

The sharp old eyes glared at him. 'Be quiet, boy! You have behaved with complete irresponsibility. You had no right to steal Dan's girl while his back was turned.'

Toby flushed and looked angrily at the old man. 'Now look here—' he began hotly.

Dan stood up, his voice cold and incisive. 'That's enough! Family wrangling won't help Aunt Kate. While she needs the comfort of hoping to get better, we're going to go on offering her that comfort. She may be weak and fanciful, as you say, Jonas, but she's very dear to all of us, I think.' His icy blue eyes swept from one face to another, one eyebrow raised in enquiry.

'Yes,' Elizabeth said, with a sense of hot shame,

'I agree with Dan—Aunt Kate comes first.'

'Very well,' said Jonas. 'What about this engagement party, then? How are you going to talk her out of that?'

Elizabeth looked blankly at him.

'We won't try,' Dan said. 'We'll tell her we're giving a party. We'll have a family party down here —she'll hear the music and voices. That will make her happy enough.'

Jonas snorted, 'Have it your own way. I wash my hands of the whole ridiculous business.' He stood up. 'Give me your arm, Toby—I'm going to take a turn around the garden.'

Toby obediently helped him towards the door. Jonas turned as he reached it and looked at Elizabeth from beneath his bristling brows.

'Aunt Kate would have been happier if you had married Dan, anyway. You're a fool, girl, a silly little fool.'

There was a long silence when he had gone. Elizabeth shifted uncomfortably on her chair, wondering what Dan was thinking.

She looked up at last and found his eyes fixed on the window. His profile was calmly reflective, and he appeared unaware of her.

'What was Karen saying to you yesterday?' he asked suddenly, swinging round to face her.

Her cheeks grew hot. 'Karen?' she stammered, trying to think of something to answer.

'Yes,' he repeated, 'Karen!' The cold blue eyes were suddenly filled with wicked amusement. 'You were deep in intimate confidences when I saw you—was she telling you the story of her life, or were you unburdening yourself to her?'

He was trying to find out how much Karen had given away, she realised.

'She was talking about a private matter,' she answered, her gaze holding his, a spark of contempt in her face.

He waited, and when she did not go on, leaned forward. 'You looked very serious, both of you!'

'Did we?' She tried to keep her face and voice expressionless.

'Karen has been very worried about Aunt Kate,' he said, after a long pause. 'She's always been very fond of her, of course, and I'm afraid she discovered how ill Aunt Kate was before the rest of us—Dr Flint told her.' A frown crossed his face and he looked fixedly at nothing.

Elizabeth only knew Dr Flint by reputation. Her parents did not approve of him. He was young, forceful, rather brusque. Her father always said he had no bedside manner. Dr Flint was too modern to think that that mattered.

'I'm surprised Dr Flint hasn't been frank with Aunt Kate,' she said now. 'My father always says he's too direct in his dealings with patients. He's reputed to have a sharp and overbearing manner.'

'He can be brutally frank,' Dan agreed. 'But not with old ladies like Aunt Kate. I was pleasantly surprised by his gentleness with her. It was he who told me to let her go on hoping—he said hope was the only medicine left for her.'

'That sounds very understanding and human,' Elizabeth said quietly. 'Perhaps his reputation isn't fair to him. Of course, my father is old-fashioned in his view of what a doctor should be like. He prefers smooth manners and a certain amount of sugar coating on the pill.'

'I hold no brief for Flint,' Dan said tautly. 'I don't like the man.'

Elizabeth looked at him in surprise. 'No? Why not?'

Dan hesitated. 'Oh, personal reasons,' he said abruptly.

That evening, after dinner, Elizabeth volunteered to wash up and make the coffee while Aunt Alice sat with Aunt Kate upstairs. She was eating all her meals at Whitebriars for the present, since Aunt Kate enjoyed her company, and it made it possible for Aunt Alice to take time off from her sickroom duties now and then.

Dan sauntered into the kitchen to dry up for her, and when he had finished, leaned against the wall watching her lazily as she made the coffee.

She found it hard to concentrate with his mocking gaze upon her. He looked altogether too dangerously attractive.

She had just arranged the cups on the tray, and was about to carry the whole thing through into the sitting-room, when Dan moved with lightning speed to intercept her. Liz looked up in startled surprise, and found his face inches from her own.

His eyes mocked. 'Lovely Liz,' he murmured. 'Do you know what you do to me?' She shivered as his mouth moved warmly down her neck. 'My gorgeous, desirable redhead!'

She put her hands on his chest to push him away.

'Let me go, Dan! What do you think you're doing?'

He laughed, sliding his hands around her waist and holding her prisoner, wedged between his body and the kitchen cupboards.

'What I should have done a long time ago,' he told her in a warm, teasing voice which made her feel hollow with love and longing for one terrible moment.

Then she remembered Karen, and her eyes grew bitterly scornful. 'Let me go, or I'll kick you!'

His face came nearer, the light in his blue eyes dazzling her. She found herself looking at the clean, hard lines of his mouth, and knew that if she stayed in his arms a second longer she would find her knees giving way.

Her toe caught him hard on the ankle bone, and he dropped his arms, wincing in recoil. She twisted out of his way and reached down the sugar bowl, placing it on the tray.

'Little beast!' he said behind her. 'I should have known you would do just as you said, shouldn't I? How many times have you unmercifully attacked me in the past? As soon as you could walk you launched yourself at me like a miniature army.'

'You deserved every slap,' she said, tossing her head.

'All the same,' he murmured calmly, 'you don't fool me, Liz! You wanted me to kiss you. You were shaking like a leaf.'

She wanted to kick him again. Icily, she said, 'Your effrontery is staggering! If I was shaking, it was with pure rage!'

He stole a lump of sugar, nibbled it, gazing at her, a little smile of infuriating amusement hovering round his mouth.

'Was it?'

'Yes,' she told him in her most biting tone. 'You can cross me off your list, Dan! I have no intention of flirting with you in corners.'

The blue eyes iced over. 'You're taking a high-minded, virtuous stand, Liz. Forgive me if I find it a little suspect. These principles of yours didn't stop you flirting with Toby while you were engaged to me, did they?'

'What about you?' she accused.

'Me?' He looked blank.

'Yes, you!' Her voice was contemptuous. 'You seem to imagine the rules are made for other people, never for yourself!'

'What the hell are you talking about?'

She caught herself up, biting her lip, and turned away. Picking up the tray, she walked to the door. 'Oh, forget it! It doesn't matter. You just aren't worth bothering about!'

He came after her, but as she turned, at bay,

alarmed by the ominous look in his eye, Toby opened the door and came in, giving Dan a quick, suspicious look.

'What's going on?' he asked.

Dan walked past them both without a word, and Elizabeth relaxed. 'Nothing, Toby,' she said, on a sigh.

On the following day she drove down to the village to pick up some groceries for Aunt Alice, and a few other items which her mother needed.

The woman who kept the village shop, Mrs Bembridge, was full of searching questions about Aunt Kate, Dan and Toby. It was painfully obvious that news of the mock engagement had, despite all their good intentions, percolated outwards, but that it was still sufficiently uncertain for Mrs Bembridge to dare to put a direct question. Her watchful eyes and curious stare made Elizabeth very embarrassed.

She became so annoyed that, in the end, she cut short her shopping and departed hurriedly with some of her commissions unfulfilled.

Running out of the shop in that flurried fashion, she bumped into a bulky young man, sending her bags flying. Eggs rolled over the pavement, tomatoes splattered, a bottle of orange juice rolled gently away into the road.

'Oh, good grief!' moaned the man, getting down on his haunches to help her as she distractedly tried to gather the things up. 'I'm terribly sorry,' he apologised, as he handed her the orange juice.

'It was my fault,' she said bluntly. 'I wasn't looking where I was going.' She looked up at him, and vaguely recognised him. 'It's Doctor Flint, isn't it?'

He nodded. 'Yes.' A sudden smile illumined his rather hard features. 'And you're Elizabeth Seaton, aren't you? I've seen you around.'

She stood up, gathering up her bags again. He studied the scramble of egg and tomato on the pavement.

'No hope of rescuing any of these,' he said regretfully, but with a faint twinkle. 'Will you let me replace them?'

'No, thank you,' she said firmly. 'There's really no need. Only two eggs are broken and I have several dozen here.'

He took the bags out of her hands. 'Well, let me escort you to your car, anyway.' They walked along the village street to where she had left her car.

'How is Miss Woodham?' he asked her as they stopped beside the car.

'She's very well,' Elizabeth said, as she had already done half a dozen times today.

Then she caught an odd look on his face, and realised that the vague response which she had been giving strangers would not do for him.

'I'm sorry,' she said quickly. 'I'd forgotten—you know the truth! Aunt Kate is much weaker, I think. She's quite bright and cheerful, but she looks more and more ethereal every day.'

He nodded. 'Yes. I saw her yesterday, of course.

There can be no change now, but I really meant her mental state. She seems much happier since you came back from Italy. She was full of your engagement party yesterday.'

Elizabeth bit her lip. 'Was she? Oh, dear!'

He quirked a curious eyebrow. 'Something wrong?'

'No, oh, no!' Elizabeth said quickly.

He seemed satisfied with that. 'How is Karen?' he asked. 'I haven't seen her for some time. I saw her at a distance last week, looking rather under the weather.'

Elizabeth glanced up and saw his face, unguarded for that moment, with a wistful expression in his grey eyes.

'Perhaps Aunt Kate's illness is upsetting her,' she said evasively.

He grimaced. 'Yes. I'm afraid it was very wrong of me to blurt out the truth to Karen.' He hesitated. 'We. . .I. . .at one time Karen and I were good friends, you see. I'm afraid I rather sinned against medical etiquette in telling her how serious her aunt's illness was!'

'I expect Dan would have told her, anyway,' Elizabeth said.

Dr Flint shook his head. 'No, apparently not. Dan told me that Karen was the last person I should have confided in—she's too much like her aunt, too vulnerable and highly strung! The news upset her badly.'

Dan being protective! thought Elizabeth bitterly.

He must care a great deal for Karen to be so concerned for her.

Dr Flint went on slowly, 'I haven't seen Karen much since then.' He flushed as Elizabeth looked sharply at him. 'I. . .rather enjoyed her company, you know.'

Good lord! Elizabeth thought. What a muddle! Obviously the doctor was interested in Karen. He would not know, never suspect, that Karen loved Dan!

Now I understand why Dan frowned at the mention of Doctor Flint's name, she thought. Of course, he would be sensitive to any attentions from other men towards Karen. Was he jealous?

She put her shopping in the back of the car and opened the door.

'Can I give you a lift, Doctor?' she asked politely, smiling at him.

He shook his head. 'No, thank you. I've got my own car. Perhaps I'll see you again, when I call on Miss Woodham?'

She dived into the car. 'Yes,' she told him. 'I'm spending a lot of time up at Whitebriars while Aunt Kate needs me.'

She drove back slowly, her mind preoccupied. She had not allowed herself to dwell upon Dan's advances of the previous evening, but the memory kept creeping into her head, making her colour come and go.

It was typical of a man to want to have his cake and eat it, she thought angrily. I suppose he expected me to be flattered. He can think again!

A man did not seem to need to *be* in love in order to enjoy *making* love. It had often baffled her in the past, especially when she was young, and alone in London far from home. Every young man who took her out for an evening seemed to expect to be paid in kind. Several had accused her of frigidity when she froze off their advances. She had even wondered if it could be true, since it had given her little pleasure to submit to meaningless caresses from a mere acquaintance.

Then she had come home, fallen in love with Dan, and their first kiss had made everything crystal clear. Her whole body had seemed to come alive. She had felt giddy, breathless, incredulously happy. Responding passionately, she had known why she had wanted to wait until she was really in love.

She had not altered her opinion, even now. Love was altogether too important to be debased by false coin. That was why, when Dan kissed her last night, she had been so angry, so humiliated! He had been offering her counterfeit love, while keeping his honest emotions for another girl.

It had been an insult. And what made it worse was that her treacherous body had reacted with delight. It was lucky that she had retained sufficient control. She would have died of shame if she had betrayed her true reaction. Even so, her first quiver of instinctive response to his touch had been sufficiently encouraging, and her cheeks burnt angrily as she remembered his complacent words.

The conceit of the man! It beggared description! She pitied Karen, who loved him so deeply and honestly that it was making her ill. Why couldn't Dan abandon his ambitions and marry the girl?

Elizabeth drew up outside her own home and stared bitterly through the window at the cool shade of the trees in the garden. Oh, she thought wearily, I wish Dan would hurry up and marry Karen, so that I can cut myself free, finally, and forget him!

Her mother was busy in the bedrooms when she let herself into the house. The vacuum cleaner was humming away, and when Elizabeth called her, Mrs Seaton looked round in surprise.

'Oh, hello, dear! Did you get everything?'

Elizabeth apologised. 'I just couldn't bear any more probing questions, so I shot off. I'll get the other things tomorrow.'

'Village life is very restricted,' Mrs Seaton said with a grimace. 'People like to know every detail of their neighbours' lives. That's why I hate living in the country.'

'For once I feel inclined to agree with you,' Elizabeth said. 'I ran into Dr Flint, too. He seemed quite nice.'

Mrs Seaton snorted, 'Nice? He's perfectly abominable! He came here, once, when I had a bad migraine, and was quite rude. He seemed to think I was a silly, idle woman who was always over-dramatising herself. These bad-tempered young doctors are all the same—they think they know everything.'

Elizabeth smiled soothing at her. She was amused, and her opinion of Doctor Flint went up again. Her mother always had a headache whenever someone tried to do something of which she did not approve. It was one of her little weapons against her husband and two children. Elizabeth knew better than to allow any such thought to show in her face. She was fond of her mother, of course, but that did not stop her from understanding the convoluted motives which at times governed Mrs Seaton's behaviour.

'Doctor Flint does seem to lack bedside manner,' she said quietly.

'Bedside manner? He has the bedside manner of a hippopotamus!'

Elizabeth laughed, then quickly sobered again as her mother looked sharply at her.

'Yes,' she said quickly, 'he is a little too blunt, I agree.'

'Downright rude, you mean!' snapped Mrs Seaton.

Elizabeth felt she needed time to be alone and think that evening, so she took a leisurely stroll through the fields, following the footpaths alongside the blackened stubble which was all that remained of the barley, wheat and oats which had so recently made the landscape golden.

Here and there, the hedges were singed and she lamented as she saw signs of abandoned nests. The burning of the stubble each year meant death for many small creatures. Mice, birds, insects, all perished in the holocaust, and quite often the hedges, too, were totally burnt out.

Her mood was one of dreary pessimism as she turned into a low-lying field near the road. She paused, frowning, hearing a queer sound, then broke into a run as she realised what it was she was hearing. Two boys were intent, their backs to her, kicking a small puppy, which cowered, yelping, in the hedge.

Elizabeth sprang upon them before they had time to realise her arrival, and with hard, determined slaps made them in their turn yelp with pain.

'What are you doing that for?' one asked resentfully as she paused, panting.

She gave him a fierce-eyed glare. 'You spiteful, nasty little beast! Hurting a defenceless animal! You deserve a lot worse than that. I ought to take you to your parents and demand that they whip you for it!'

The smaller of the two began to cry, but the older boy, giving her a look of hostility, said, 'They wouldn't care! They said we couldn't have the puppy because it was too much trouble! They don't want it!'

Elizabeth stared at him. 'Do you mean they told you to abandon the puppy?'

'Yes,' he spat out. 'They told us to get rid of it. They didn't care how—it was a nuisance.'

'Where did it come from originally?' she demanded.

'Someone at school gave it to me,' he said, scowling.

Elizabeth felt a burning anger. What criminal neglect! She let the boys go and bent to pick up the shivering little animal, cuddling it close to her.

'I'll look after it,' she said flatly.

The boys stared. 'What are you going to do with it? Drown it?' asked the younger boy in a voice which shook.

'No,' she said indignantly. 'I shall keep it. You don't deserve to have a puppy, anyway. You're cruel and unkind. If I ever see you doing anything like this again, I'll report you to the police. It's against the law, you know.'

The boys exchanged a look, then sped away. Elizabeth turned on to the road and began to walk along, stroking the puppy gently. It trembled all the time, its soft brown eyes rolling in its head.

'Poor little mite,' she soothed. 'You're safe now, I won't hurt you.'

Toby pulled up beside her a little while later, and grinned at her as she climbed into the car.

'I came in search of you, my love! I missed you!' Then he stared at the puppy. 'Good lord, where did you find that?' She told him, and he looked angry. 'Little horrors! Why do kids do things like that?'

'They take their attitude from their parents,' she said.

'What will you do with it?' Toby enquired.

'Keep him, I suppose,' said Liz, dropping a kiss on the smooth brown head of the little dog.

Toby grinned indulgently. 'You're too soft-hearted.' He drove on for a while, then glanced at her. 'I was congratulated on my engagement today, by the way. I'm afraid the news is out.'

'I know,' she said. 'When I was in the village I realised that some sort of rumour was going around.'

'I expect they find it fascinating—a game of marriage, with the partners changing every now and then!'

Liz flushed. 'Don't! It sounds so horrid!'

'Face facts, Liz. People are bound to see it like that. First Dan, then me! And when you break off our engagement, it's going to make them reel with laughter.'

'I knew it was a stupid idea,' she groaned. 'Telling lies always has disastrous consequences, whatever the motive.'

'Look,' he said, 'hang on to the motive—that's the important thing. We did this for Aunt Kate, and it worked. She's as cosy as a rabbit up there in her room, planning our engagement party, and never suspecting why we really flew home so suddenly.'

Elizabeth sighed, 'Yes, I know.'

He glanced at her, frowning. 'It's tough on you, love. And especially with Dan around all the time.'

Her face tightened. She did not answer. Toby watched her out of the corner of his eye.

'What was Dan up to in the kitchen last night? Is he still pursuing you? I told you he was a dangerous man. Dan is like the bulldog—he never gives up once he's got his teeth sunk into you. That's what makes him so successful. In business that never-say-die attitude pays dividends.'

'It doesn't work so badly in love, either,' she said with some bitterness.

Toby's eyes narrowed. 'He was making a pass, then? I could break his neck! Why doesn't he leave you alone?' He looked at her. 'I'd love to know the real reason why you broke off that engagement, honey. I have a nasty feeling you still find Dan attractive. But if so—why?'

Elizabeth closed her eyes wearily. 'Don't probe, Toby,' she said. 'Please! I'm too tired.'

He shrugged. 'As you like!' After a silence, he asked, 'Have you had a good look at Karen lately? She looks ill. I tried to ask her a few questions, and oddly enough got the same sort of reply.' He grinned at Elizabeth. 'Must be my personality. I get the brush-off whenever I try to help people.'

She smiled affectionately at him. 'Idiot! Karen's very fond of you. I expect she just feels as I do—that some things are too complicated to be talked about.'

'Are you fond of me, Liz?' he asked delicately, staring at the road ahead.

She looked at him in sudden surprise. 'Yes, of course I am, you madman! I always have been.'

A little flush crept into his cheeks. He turned his head to look at her, his brown eyes intent.

'I wish I knew what you meant by that,' he said softly. 'I. . .I find you very attractive, Liz!'

She was too stunned to reply for a moment.

Toby! She looked out of the window at the flash of the green hedgerows. A little cluster of sparrows flew out from under their wheels as they drove along, just missing death by inches.

'No answer?' Toby asked softly.

She looked slowly round at him. 'I don't know what to say, Toby. I. . .just didn't know!'

'Will you think about it?' he asked her tentatively. 'I don't expect an ecstatic response right now. Just let the thought of me sink into your subconscious.' His grin was half wistful, half self-deriding. 'I might grow on you!'

'I. . .wish I could believe that,' she said suddenly. 'Toby, I really wish I loved you. You're so nice, and you would be so nice to love.'

He grimaced. 'Don't put it like that, love. That's negative thinking. Every day, when you get up, say to yourself, Toby is lovable. I could love Toby.' He winked. 'It may work!'

CHAPTER SEVEN

'WHAT will you call him?' Dan asked, his long brown fingers gently fondling the puppy's ears.

'I haven't thought of a name yet,' Liz answered, feeling a ludicrous pang of envy as she watched the strong hands moving to gather the little dog up against Dan's chest, where, wriggling ecstatically, the pup tried to lick Dan's smiling, averted face.

'Stop that, you silly little snip,' Dan murmured, holding his head back. He shot Elizabeth an amused look. 'Solomon isn't going to approve of his arrival,' he said.

'No,' she smiled back, forgetting her dislike of him for the moment. 'Solomon loathes dogs and has a strong sense of his own importance. I shudder to think what his reaction will be!'

'He hasn't seen him yet?'.

'No—Solomon had a night out last night. I took the pup up to my room because he howled whenever we left him alone.' She grinned. 'I have no doubt that Solomon knows a dog has been in the house, though. He always knows everything that goes on, of course. He's too clever by half.'

Dan's blue eyes danced at her. 'I expect the pup will soon ingratiate himself. Look at him. . .'

holding the little animal up so that she could see the warm, confiding shine of the brown eyes, the snub nose and small pink tongue.

Liz bent forward to kiss the puppy's black nose. 'He's adorable! Who could bear to hurt him?'

'What was your mother's reaction to his arrival? Horror, I imagine! She's never liked having animals around.'

She grimaced. 'She wasn't exactly delighted! She's used to Solomon now, and of course, he's so self-sufficient and beautifully clean. Luckily, the pup seems to be house-trained. She got a little cross when he kept crying last night, but that stopped when I took him to my room.'

'You mustn't let him keep that up,' Dan frowned. 'Dogs need discipline. He must sleep downstairs, Liz. He won't keep crying for long if you ignore him.'

She gave him a grin. 'You haven't heard the noise he makes! He sounds like a banshee!'

Dan shook his head, grinning. 'You'll spoil him!' He sat back in his chair, stroking the smooth brown head. 'Aunt Kate has had a very bad night,' he said more soberly.

'Oh, no! Is she worse?'

'Considerably, I would say. She looks so frail that a puff of wind could blow her away.' He sighed. 'Yet she seems very contented. She talked about her childhood most of the time.'

Liz shot him an intent glance. 'Did you sit up with her?'

His face was blank. 'Yes,' he said tersely.

'All night?' she probed.

The blue eyes were vague. He murmured something she did not catch, but which she sensed to be in the affirmative.

'No wonder you have shadows under your eyes this morning,' she scolded. 'Do you intend to work today?'

'As you see, I've taken the morning off,' he said lightly. 'Toby is holding the fort for me, and your father is there in case of an emergency. Between them, they can manage.'

'You should have gone to bed and stayed there all day,' she said.

Dan looked at her, his eyes wide and direct. 'I was afraid to,' he said bluntly.

'Because. . .in case Aunt Kate. . .' her voice broke on the last words and Dan's hand shot out to seize hers and squeeze it.

'Yes,' he said huskily.

They looked at each other in silence. His thumb moved slowly up and down the back of her hand, and her pulses quivered in response.

'We shall miss her, shan't we, Liz? There'll be a big gap in all our lives.'

'Yes,' she said, her eyes misty. 'And I wish. . .' her words stopped suddenly. I wish I hadn't had to hurt her by breaking off our engagement, she had meant to say. She knew Aunt Kate had been upset by that. It was sad that she should have done anything to make Aunt Kate's last days less happy than they might have been. If she had known. . .

Dan bent forward, his eyes searching hers, their expression warm and gentle. 'You wish what, Liz?'

She could not break away from that compelling gaze. She felt weak and helpless under the spell of those blue eyes. He waited, one eyebrow crooked quizzically, yet without impatience, as though he could read her thoughts, and was only waiting for her to admit them to him.

There was a cough behind them, and they both looked round. Doctor Flint stood in the open french windows, his black bag in his hand, grinning at them.

'Sorry to disturb you,' he said cheerfully. 'I rang the bell, but there was no answer, so I came round the back. I thought you might all be out in the garden.'

Elizabeth hurriedly stood up. 'Oh, dear, the bell must be out of order! How lucky that you came round the back!'

'I knew someone must be about,' he said. 'I knew you wouldn't all have gone out and left Miss Woodham alone.'

'My aunt is sitting with her,' Dan said, standing with the puppy in his arms.

Doctor Flint put out a hand to touch the dog's head. 'That's a pretty little creature! You're brave, taking on a puppy when you have illness in the house!'

'It's my dog,' Elizabeth said, taking the pup from Dan, and submitting to his eager caress, smiling as he struggled to cover her face with his tongue.

'You shouldn't let him lick you,' Doctor Flint said. 'Very unhygienic!'

Dan gave him a contemptuous glance. 'I'll take you up to my aunt's room,' he said coolly.

Elizabeth went into the kitchen when they had gone, and made some coffee. Dan joined her a few moments later. The puppy had curled up on the doormat and was fast asleep.

Dan looked at him with amusement. 'I wonder what he dreams about? See how his nose is twitching?'

'Why don't you like Doctor Flint, Dan?' she asked irrelevantly. 'He seems quite pleasant, despite his reputation. I know my mother doesn't care for him much, but then he trod on her toes. He's one of those doctors who have no time for imaginary ailments, and my mother, bless her heart, has always used her headaches to get her own way.'

Dan nodded. 'Yes, I remember those headaches of hers when we were young! Your mother always hated living in the country. She's a born city-dweller.'

'She's put up with it, for Dad's sake, though,' Liz pointed out. 'She's never tried to persuade him to live anywhere else.'

'Because she hoped he would take over the firm one day,' Dan said coolly.

Elizabeth flushed. 'Is that so wrong? Of course she wanted him to succeed.'

'And what does he want?' Dan's eyes were narrowed. 'I've often wondered. He dislikes me—he always did! Under that bland exterior your father has ambitions of his own.'

'You're wrong,' she flared at once. 'Dad is perfectly happy.' Yet she could not help remembering her father's odd reaction when she told him she had broken her engagement. He had seemed almost amused, as though it pleased him to think that Dan was going to fail in something at last. Was her father envious of Dan?

'Is he?' Dan grimaced. 'I wonder! Do we ever really know what goes on in people's minds?'

She looked round into his face, her eyes challenging. 'I certainly don't know what goes on in yours!'

His blue eyes held hers, their expression unreadable. 'Do you want to know?'

She felt a breathless sense of panic. Dan had always had this effect on her, threatening to swamp her own identity, to dominate and subjugate her.

She backed slightly, trembling. 'No,' she said quickly. 'No, I don't think I do!'

He smiled tightly. 'Sure?' he asked mockingly.

She turned away, stumbling over her own feet in her haste to break the spell which bound them. But Dan grabbed her shoulders and pulled her round to face him again.

'Oh, no,' he said grimly. 'You can't get away that easily. You provoked this situation. You talk about not knowing what goes on in my mind. Do you even understand your own? I'm beginning to think you're as blind about yourself as you are about me!'

'I'm not blind,' Liz retorted, her temper flaring. 'I know you better than you think! All that puzzles me is how you have the insolence to flirt with me while you. . .' she stopped sharply. She would not mention Karen. If he knew that she had found out about Karen, he would leap to the conclusion that she was jealous. As I am, she thought miserable. As I am!

'While I what?' he asked impatiently. 'I'm getting sick and tired of your hints, Liz. If I've done something—tell me, for heaven's sake!'

'Please,' she said, in pretended indifference, 'let me go! Toby wouldn't like to see you mauling me about!'

Dan's face tightened and an angry red came into his face. 'Toby!' he said, with the force of an expletive. 'Damn Toby!' Then he had pulled her up against him, his hands bruising her shoulders, and his mouth forced itself down on her lips with demanding hunger.

Elizabeth struggled furiously at first, pushing and hitting at his chest, but he was as immovable as a rock, and gradually her body asserted itself above the rational rejection of her mind.

She felt herself go limp, her hands slowly flattened on his chest, feeling the heat of his body through his shirt, then moved involuntarily up to his neck and caressed the crisp dark hair at the back of his head. He slid his hands down her back, pulling her closer, and she melted against him, responding to his kisses with a heat that matched his own.

'Liz,' he murmured, burying his face in her throat. 'Lovely, desirable Liz, I knew you couldn't be as indifferent as you pretended. . .'

Pride gave her the strength to wrench herself away. Breathless and flushed, she glared at him. 'Don't flatter yourself! Just because I let you kiss me! What does that mean? You're despicable, Dan—you want to have your cake and eat it, too. Well, I'm not prepared to play your double game. I happen to believe that if you're not in love with someone you shouldn't flirt with them.'

'You were flirting with me,' he said, his voice as rough as her own.

'You misunderstood me,' she retorted. 'You know, Dan, you're the sort of man who only wants something when it's out of reach. You want me now because I belong to Toby. When I was engaged to you, I hardly ever saw you. You let me go without a murmur, because you didn't want me. Then you felt aggrieved because you thought you had lost something which might have amused you.'

He stared at her. 'What are you talking about? I admit, we saw very little of each other when we were engaged—but that was partly because I was so busy at the factory, and partly. . .' he stopped, reddening.

She waited, raising an ironic eyebrow. 'Partly what, Dan?'

He looked directly at her, his mouth taut. 'Partly

because I avoided seeing you too often,' he admitted.

It hurt, even though she had known it. 'So I was right,' she said wearily.

'The hell you were!' he said forcefully. 'I avoided seeing you because when I was with you I couldn't keep my hands off you, and that damned father of yours had forced us to wait a year before we got married. I knew I was going to find it unbearable to wait that long, but I'd given my word. So I had to play it cool.'

Her eyes fell before the look in his, and she said weakly, 'Oh!' She did not doubt him for an instant. His eyes were too direct. Had that been why he fell in love with Karen? Because he was feeling frustrated and lonely?

He leaned against the sink, watching her. 'I know I was often bad-tempered and surly in those days. Now you know why! I was feeling like hell.' He shrugged. 'It may be different for a woman. A man isn't built to wait for months when he's madly in love.'

Elizabeth stared at the floor as though it fascinated her. 'Were you, Dan?'

'Was I what?'

'In love?'

There was a long silence. She looked up quickly and found his blue eyes fixed on the ceiling, his face a cold mask.

After a moment, he said, 'That's the most cutting question you could have asked me. I feel as though

I've never even known you, Liz. How can you do it? Does it give you some sort of twisted pleasure to slap my face like that?' His eyes came down to her face, contempt in them. 'You make me sorry I ever met you!'

She was bewildered, anxious, now. Had she, after all, been wrong? She looked at him in puzzled enquiry, but before she could ask the question she most wanted to know the answer to, the door opened and Doctor Flint came in with a smile.

'Hello! Just dropped by to say that I'm leaving.'

Dan straighted and gave him a cool nod. 'How is Aunt Kate?'

The young man shrugged, his expression sombre. 'Well, you know the situation. No change. It may be any time now.'

'I see,' said Dan flatly.

Doctor Flint hesitated. 'I'll try to call again this evening.'

Dan nodded. 'I'll walk to the door with you,' he said, and passed him into the hall.

Doctor Flint smiled at Elizabeth. 'Your aunt was asking for you. Will you go up? She seems very excited about this party—she asked me to come.' His grey eyes looked appealingly into hers. 'Is that all right?'

Elizabeth flushed. 'Yes, of course,' she said, hoping that Aunt Kate would not invite anyone else. They had planned to have the party that evening, since it had become an obsession with the old lady, as if she felt that the party had some

personal significance. Elizabeth wondered if Aunt
Kate thought that it would somehow strengthen her
to hear life going on as usual around her. It was
hard to keep up a pretence of normal life, to have
gay conversations in her hearing, to laugh and talk
about the silly little things of life, just as though she
were not so very ill. Yet they all kept up this
pretence, despite the strain it imposed upon them.

Doctor Flint looked hopefully at her. 'You mean
that? I shan't be an intruder?'

'Of course not,' she protested.

She carried the coffee upstairs with her when she
went to see Aunt Kate, leaving some for Dan on the
kitchen table. She passed him in the hall, and
briefly told him to drink his coffee while it was hot.
He nodded without reply.

Aunt Alice was sitting beside the bed, knitting a
pale blue sweater for Karen, while Aunt Kate dozed
gently, her head back against her pillows. Elizabeth
smiled across the room, putting the tray down on
the bedside table on the other side of the bed.

At the clink of the china Aunt Kate opened her
eyes and gave herself a little shake. 'There you are,
Liz dear,' she said. 'Did you see my nice doctor?
Isn't he sweet? Such a kind, thoughtful young man.
He brought me the latest thriller.' And she indicated
a gaudy paperback which lay on the white quilt.

Aunt Alice rolled up her knitting. 'If you're going
to sit with her, I'll nip down to start the prep-
arations for lunch,' she told Liz.

'Will you have coffee first? I brought up a cup for you.'

'No, thank you, my dear. I prefer a cup of tea.' Aunt Alice gave her a polite smile and left the room. Elizabeth sighed. Aunt Alice had been very reserved since their return from Italy. Elizabeth imagined that it was because she resented the fact that Toby was being used to keep Aunt Kate happy. If his mother guessed that Toby was really fond of her, Elizabeth mentally acknowledged, then she would see this false engagement as a form of betrayal.

'Well, are you looking forward to the party?' Aunt Kate demanded, with a child's eagerness.

Elizabeth smiled back, touched by the old lady's unchanging delight in life. She was not giving in to the illness which was eating up her energy and strength. She was trying to keep up a pretence of normal life, reading her favourite books, looking forward to little treats, laughing and responding with the same warmth to those around her. It made Elizabeth ashamed. Really, she was mean-spirited, to begrudge Aunt Kate the small sacrifice of a few days out of her life. Perhaps it had been foolish of them to invent this engagement. They might have been able to think of some other, less difficult, story to account for a sudden return from Italy. But all the same, what did all that matter, compared with bringing Aunt Kate pleasure?

They sat, talking about the party for some time; Aunt Kate questioning her about the food which had been laid on, about the people who were coming, sighing over her own inability to be downstairs on this occasion.

'But I shall for your wedding, dear. Oh, yes, I shall be there at your wedding! I wouldn't miss it for worlds.' And the faded blue eyes closed slowly, as sleep caught up with her.

Elizabeth's hand closed over the thin, gnarled fingers. 'Yes,' she said softly, 'you'll be there!'

Aunt Kate smiled, half asleep. 'Dear Liz. I. . .never married, you know. I've so looked forward to seeing you young people marry. Weddings are such delightful occasions. I always weep— I just can't help it.' She yawned.

'Yes, Aunt Kate,' Elizabeth said gently.

'Dan will make a wonderful husband,' Aunt Kate added drowsily.

Elizabeth's hand stiffened. She sat back, looking at the small, wrinkled face. Aunt Kate's lips parted. A faint sound came slowly, the soft breathing of sleep.

Of couse! Elizabeth thought. She had forgotten, for the moment. Her mind had slipped back to the days when Elizabeth had been going to marry Dan. It was lucky that nobody else had been around to overhear that remark, though, or to see the hot flush which Aunt Kate's words had brought.

Tears pricked at her eyes. Oh, why had it all gone wrong? Why did Dan have to fall in love with Karen? If he had been honest earlier, he had, after all, once been in love with her. Her fear that he had wanted to marry her purely for business reasons had been unjust and petty. Dan had been being perfectly honest when he said that it had been that long engagement which brought about the change—she did not doubt him now. She was not a man. She did not know how their minds and hearts worked. But she could imagine that the long frustration of that engagement had operated just as Dan had claimed—making him irritable, impatient, restless.

And of course, Karen had been down at the factory every day, and in his house in the evenings. Sweet, gentle, soothing Karen, always on hand to smooth his troubled brow!

She walked across the bedroom softly, so as not to wake Aunt Kate, and stared at herself in the dressing-table mirror. Her red hair, tanned skin and slender figure showed to perfection against the simple white dress she wore.

I could win Dan back, she thought suddenly, her mouth growing taut. He wouldn't have made love to me like that if he hadn't still found me attractive.

Her heart leapt, her pulses began to race and she saw her eyes shining with hope. She stared at that revealing reflection, seeing the tell-tale little pulse at the base of her throat beating like mad.

Wouldn't it be easy? Dan had been different since she got back from Italy. It was, as she had told him in anger, very obvious that he found her tempting now that she was placed beyond his reach.

Her chin went up aggressively. I could take him

away from Karen very easily. After all, she stole him from me. I would be justified in fighting to get him back.

Then the light went out of her eyes, and she turned away, her shoulders drooping. No, she thought coldly. I can't do it. Karen loves him so much.

She remembered the white anguish in Karen's face, the stammered confession the other girl had once made her. What had she said? That she had made a mess of falling in love, that she was shy and insecure about her lover?

And with good reason, Elizabeth thought coldly. What sort of man was Dan, anyway? Had he no integrity? Dan must be forced to stick to his bargain now. He had made Karen fall in love with him. He would have to marry her.

She went back to the bed and sat down quietly, picking up Aunt Kate's paperback.

When the old lady woke up Elizabeth offered to read to her, and they spent a happy hour together, unravelling the tense threads of a rather nerve-racking thriller.

Then Dan came in, with the puppy under his arm, and Aunt Kate gave a little cry of delight. 'Oh, the darling! Where did he come from? He isn't yours, Dan?'

'No,' said Dan, grinning at her. 'He belongs to Elizabeth.' He did not tell Aunt Kate how the pup had come into Elizabeth's possession, nor did Elizabeth. The horrible story would only hurt and bewilder Aunt Kate, who was incapable of such cold-hearted callousness to helpless animals. Elizabeth could remember the old lady's shock when she read in the newspapers of boys tormenting a swan on the nearby river. Aunt Kate had been baffled and horrorstruck.

Dan dropped the puppy on the bed and he wriggled under Aunt Kate's fondling hands, licking her fingers.

'He'll make a terrible mess in that bed,' said Elizabeth, bending to remove him.

'Oh, what does it matter?' Dan said curtly, his hand pulling her back.

Aunt Kate was too intent on the puppy to see the long look they exchanged, a lok of hostility and armed dislike.

Smiling happily, Aunt Kate pulled one of the pup's soft ears. 'What is he called?'

'I haven't given him a name yet,' Elizabeth told her. 'Perhaps you can think of one!'

'I had a dog when I was little,' Aunt Kate said reminiscently. 'He was called Charlie. He was killed in an accident.'

They watched her indulgently, smiling. She had that faraway look in her eyes again, thought Elizabeth, as if she was seeing other times and other people. From time to time she lapsed into the past, re-living old forgotten memories. The long gap between childhood and age seemed to have closed up for her. She talked of herself, sometimes, as though life was just beginning for her. As,

Elizabeth thought gently, perhaps it was!

Aunt Kate looked up at them. 'Charlie is a very nice name for a little dog, isn't it?' she asked hopefully.

Elizabeth nodded. 'I like it! Shall we call him Charlie, then, Aunt Kate?'

The faded blue eyes returned to the puppy. 'Charlie,' she breathed, taking his little face in her two thin hands. 'Hello, Charlie!'

He panted, his tongue hanging out, and gave a wheezy sort of yap.

Aunt Kate laughed. 'There, he knows that's his name!' She lay back, looking at them, her face suddenly very pale. 'I think I'll have another little nap now.'

Aunt Alice came in quietly and sat down beside the bed. Dan picked up the puppy and he and Elizabeth went softly out of the room.

Lunch was laid out on the dining-room table—a large bowl of mixed salad, a plate of sliced pink ham, cheese, boiled eggs in mayonnaise, bread and butter, fruit juice and a fresh fruit salad.

Dan and Jonas ate in silence, their eyes bent on their plates. Elizabeth looked at them from time to time, thinking how alike they were. Dan would look just like his grandfather when he was old. Already his rugged good looks shadowed the hawklike profile, the dominating nose and sharp, bright eyes of the old man.

Jonas looked up and caught her glance. He grinned at her. 'Looking forward to the party tonight? We're to have dancing, I hear! Just to please Kate!'

'It's making her happy,' said Elizabeth.

He nodded. 'Oh, I know! Sentimental old fool.' But his tone lacked conviction, and she sensed that beneath his brusque no-nonsense attitude he was very fond of his sister, and grieved by her illness.

'She wants Toby and myself to go up and see her,' she said in as matter-of-fact a way as she could manage.

Dan looked up, his eyes narrowed. 'What for? Some sort of family blessing?'

'We are supposed to be engaged,' she pointed out coolly.

He sneered, 'Supposed to be! Yes!'

Jonas laughed, looking from one to the other of their tense, angry faces.

'You never know, Liz, you and Toby might get to like being engaged. Might decide to carry on with it!' He shot his grandson a bright, teasing look. 'After all, Liz is a damned pretty girl. Toby could do worse.'

'Thank you, Jonas,' Elizabeth said tartly.

Dan's eyes held hers. 'Is that likely?' His voice was hard and cold.

She shrugged, defying his challenge. 'You never know, as Jonas said!'

Dan laughed cynically. 'I should have warned Toby! I have a notion he doesn't intend to tie himself down yet.'

She smiled sweetly at him. 'Oh, you're wrong!

Toby likes being engaged to me!'

Dan laid down his spoon and pushed his fruit
salad away, half eaten.

'I must get down to the factory,' he said to Jonas.
'I have a pile of work to get through.'

Jonas watched him walk out, grinning. Then he
looked at Elizabeth with a twinkle.

'I enjoyed that!'

She shook her head at him reprovingly. 'I don't
know what you mean!'

'You've got Dan in a corner,' he said with high
amusement. 'I often used to wonder if the boy was
capable of getting himself in an emotional muddle.'
His face grew almost serious and he went on slowly:
'People who can't feel deeply are never fully alive,
my dear. It's only by making mistakes and learning
from them that we change and mature. Dan has
been too good at everything. He made no mistakes
in business. He was cool-headed, clever and confident. It worried me at times. That was why it
pleased me to see him falling in love with you—if he
had chosen some doormat, or even worse, some
cold fashion-plate, I would have hated it.'

'What makes you so sure he's in love with me?'
Elizabeth asked slowly.

He gave her a scathing look. 'I'm too old to be
fooled. At first, I wasn't sure that you were going to
manage to control him. You were so obviously crazy
about him. Dan swept you off your feet in a matter
of days.'

She flushed angrily. 'Was I so obvious?'

The cool old eyes smiled. 'I'm afraid so, my dear. It was blazingly apparent to everyone. Your father and I talked it over.'

'My father?' She sat up, her eyes intent. 'What did you talk over?'

'Your relationship with Dan,' he said. 'We agreed that if you married Dan at once, you would be eaten alive. Dan is too tough, too domineering to let a woman govern him. And you, my dear, were so much in love that you would have given in all along the line. So we decided a year's wait would be good for both of you.'

Elizabeth was very still now, her face tight with anger. 'So it was your idea, after all!'

He nodded. 'Your father agreed with me, though! James is a little jealous of Dan—always was. But he was right on this occasion. Dan needed to learn something—and you were the person to teach him.'

'What was I supposed to teach him?' she asked very quietly, her hands locked in her lap to prevent them from shaking.

'That he wasn't God,' said Jonas lightly. 'That he couldn't just reach up and pick the best apple off the tree at will.'

'So I was the instrument you chose, you and my father, to cut Dan down to size!'

He gave her an astonished look. 'You sound quite annoyed, my dear!'

'Annoyed? I'm damned angry!'

'Tut, tut,' he said with amusement. 'I don't like

to hear a young girl swear!'

'Then you'd better shut your ears,' she said furiously, 'because I frankly feel like using a great many swear words! Did it ever occur to either of you that it was you that was playing God? Or that it might be me, and not Dan, who would get hurt in the process?'

He stared at her. 'My dear child, what do you mean?'

She opened her mouth, words seething on her tongue, then shut it again.

'Oh, no,' she said, 'I'm not going to unpack my thoughts for you, ever again, Jonas! You manipulate everyone who put themselves in your grasp. From now on, I shall steer clear of you! And if you want my advice, you won't let Dan know that it was your idea to make us wait for a year. He might be less forbearing than I am. Your age might not protect you!'

She jumped up and walked out of the room, leaving him staring after her with drawn brows.

CHAPTER EIGHT

SHE WALKED home to change for the party, and found Tom lying on the lawn in an attitude of total relaxation, his arms stretched above his head.

'Lazybones!' she said, poking him gently with her foot.

He half opened one eye to grin. 'Not me! I've just mowed the lawn and it's knocked me out!'

She glanced around at the billiard-table smoothness of the grass.

'Amazing! Keep taking the pills!' Then, dropping down beside him, she asked, 'Are you coming to the party?'

Tom looked up at her, his face oddly inverted, his expression unreadable.

'This pretended engagement party—what's the point?'

'You know?' She sighed. 'I see. Jonas!'

'Did you think he'd keep it to himself?' Tom rolled over and propped his chin upon his hands. 'He was knocked flat when you came back apparently engaged to Toby. It really fluttered the family dovecote. When Jonas found out it was all a put-up job for Aunt Kate's sake, he rushed round to break the great news to the parents.'

Elizabeth grimaced. 'I can just imagine! I should have held my tongue, but I'd lost my temper.'

Tom swivelled his eyes sideways. 'With Dan, of course?'

'Why of course?' she evaded.

'Because, despite breaking the engagement, you're still hooked on him,' Tom said quietly.

She plucked a piece of grass and twiddled it around in her fingers.

'That's one way of putting it,' she said slowly.

'Why did you break the engagement?'

Liz looked up at the sky and watched the slow passage of the clouds with eyes that saw nothing. 'I found out that he was having a fling with Karen,' she said.

Tom sat up abruptly and stared at her. '*What* did you say?'

She was taken aback by his tone, and looked at him in mild surprise. She repeated her words, and saw his face harden into a pale mask.

'Good God! I would never have believed it! Little Karen? She must be out of her skull—Dan would never do for her.' Tom leaned forward. 'Look, are you sure about this?'

'I saw them together,' Elizabeth said. 'I overheard enough to be quite certain. They were talking about me. . .saying they hated to hurt me, hoped I would never find out the truth. I felt sick, as you can imagine. I went away, thought about it, and decided to break the engagement without letting on that I knew about them.'

'So they don't know you found out?' Tom asked slowly.

'No. I thought that it would only make them miserable if they knew I'd been hurt. I imagined they would get married quite soon, of course.'

'But they haven't,' he pointed out. 'And I see them every day at the factory. If they *are* in love, they hide it very well. I've never seen any sign of it.'

Liz sighed wearily. 'Dan's a very good actor.'

'Granted,' Tom agreed. 'He's a superb poker player. But why haven't they come out into the open now, when they're perfectly free to do so? Why go on hiding it?'

'I did suspect that Dan wanted to marry me for the family stock,' she said. 'Mother hinted at it—said Dan would like to get control of my share of the Woodham stock so that he could get a majority holding.' She glanced at him. 'It sounded possible at the time.'

'But now?' Tom probed.

'I'm not so sure. He. . .he may have had that in mind. I do think he was genuinely in love with me at one time. It was the long engagement that ruined everything—he was bored, Karen was there, and the rest is obvious.'

'So we're back to the question of why no announcement of a marriage between him and Karen?'

'Yes,' she agreed. 'And I don't know the answer, unless it's that Dan isn't sure of his feelings, while Karen is.' She looked at him frankly. 'Tom, Karen is hopelessly in love. She admitted as much to me, although she didn't name the man. I find it easy to hate Dan, but I couldn't hate Karen. She's suffered so much over this!'

'Poor Karen,' he said heavily, frowning.

Liz stood up and smoothed down her white skirt, brushing off some loose grass.

'A pity she didn't fall for Doctor Flint,' she said lightly.

Tom joined her and asked casually, 'Why Flint, for heaven's sake?'

'Oh, just a fancy I had! He asked me about her, and I got the impression that he rather liked her.'

'He's as wrong for her as Dan,' Tom said. 'Both of them would ride roughshod over her, and Karen is made of softer metal than most girls. She needs gentle handling.'

Elizabeth looked at him curiously. His tone had held some indefinable roughness, as though he was angry. It was rare for easy-going, lazy Tom to get worked up about anything. He took life very much as it came, accepting what happened with cheerful fatalism.

They went into the house and found their parents talking in the kitchen. James Seaton looked round, breaking off abruptly. Elizabeth looked at him coolly.

'I've been having an illuminating chat with Jonas today, Dad,' she said challengingly.

He smiled blandly. 'Yes, he said as much to me on the telephone earlier. You got a little hot under the collar, I gather.'

'A little? I was furious!'

Tom leaned against the wall, watching them with an amused smile. Elizabeth faced her father, her chin up belligerently, her green eyes sparkling angrily at him. Very relaxed, his urbane manner unchanged, James Seaton watched her in his turn, a little smile on his mouth.

'You're being unreasonable, my dear,' he said quietly. 'We did what we thought best for both of you. My chief concern, I freely admit, was your own welfare.'

'My welfare!' The words were flung at him scornfully. 'You were trying to beat Dan, using me as the stick!'

'I thought, and Jonas agreed with me, that Dan was not ready for marriage yet,' he returned easily. 'Marriage is supposed to be a partnership, a compromise between two people, and with two people like you and Dan that means a great deal. You're both of you very intelligent, very head-strong, reckless of consequence and determined on your own way. One of you would have had to give way, or be badly hurt in the process.' He gave her a long, thoughtful look. 'Jonas and I both thought that the one who would have to give way would be you, Liz. You were the weaker of the two at that time.'

'Oh, was I?' she retorted, still angry.

'Yes,' he said gently. 'You were very much in love with Dan. Oh, I think he loved you, but he was so much older, so much more sure of himself. He would have used your love as a weapon against you. Had you been less strong-minded that might not have been disastrous. You would have gradually become Dan's willing echo.'

Her face burned angrily. 'I would never have been anyone's slave, Dad! You don't know me if you ever thought that!'

'I do know you,' he said softly. 'That's why I knew that a year's delay would give you a chance to learn how to deal with Dan, let you see what you were up against. I knew that your own will would develop sufficient strength to permit you to stand up to Dan and win, on occasions.' He laughed, eyeing her face with a wry amusement. 'And also it would have made Dan that much more malleable. He would value you more because he had been forced to wait for you.'

She laughed, too, but with bitter irony. 'It didn't work out like that, did it? You and Jonas played God, and just messed up our lives for us.'

He shook his head. 'No—we were right. I admit, when you broke your engagement, that it was a shock, but then I saw that you still cared about Dan, and I was prepared to wait. I thought you would come together again. And next time the balance would be more even. Dan would have learnt more patience, be prepared to compromise with you.'

Elizabeth eyed him soberly. 'You should have left it to us, Dad. You shouldn't have interfered.'

Then she walked out of the room, leaving an

uncomfortable silence behind her.

Mrs Seaton stared at her husband. 'So that's what it was all about! How could you, James? You've ruined their lives!'

'Nonsense,' he said equably. 'I've given them the chance to be very happy together. Had she married Dan right away, they would have ended in the divorce courts. Dan was too domineering.'

'She was right,' Mrs Seaton said bitterly. 'You used your own daughter as a weapon in your fight against Dan! You've always resented him. He was everything you could never be—successful, clever, ambitious. Dan will be a millionaire one day. He has the magic touch. You've always claimed to be contented as you are, James, but I begin to wonder!'

'My dear,' he said wryly, 'I am content, I assure you. It's you who are discontented. I'm sorry if I haven't lived up to your expectations. I've never wanted to be a tycoon. All I wanted was a happy family life.' He spread his hands helplessly. 'I knew, of course, that you had higher ambitions, but one pays for such a success, my dear. That's why I didn't want Liz to pay for Dan's ambition.'

Mary Seaton stared at him silently. Then she bit her lip. 'I. . .I have been very happy, James, and I couldn't love you more however successful you were! Of course I wanted you to climb to the very top. What woman doesn't want her man to do that? But I couldn't stop loving you just because you weren't as ambitious as I would like!' Her voice broke. 'Oh, you know very well I've always loved you in spite of everything!'

Tom, quietly sliding out of the room, heard his father say gently, 'My dear Mary! Of course I know that!'

Mary Seaton ran to him and buried her face against her husband's shoulder.

James raised her face and smiled at her. 'And you believe me when I say that what I did, in delaying Liz's wedding, was done for the best intentions?'

She sighed. 'Yes, I suppose so! I'm afraid it didn't succeed, though.'

'We shall see,' said her husband, kissing her. 'We shall see, my dear!'

The Seatons drove round to Whitebriars together in style. Tom looked unusually elegant in a dark lounge suit, very modern in cut.

Elizabeth wore the midnight-blue dress which she had worn at the cricket club dance. She had brushed her own hair until it shone like burnished red-gold, then swept it up at the back of her head in a smooth chignon.

Dan opened the door to them, smiling politely. His face, as Elizabeth passed him, tightened.

'You look very lovely tonight,' he said huskily, and she felt her pulses leap in pleasure.

Then Toby came out to greet them, eyes dancing.

'Hello, love! How's the puppy? Aunt Kate tells

me you're going to call him Charlie—sounds very suitable.'

'Don't mention that animal!' groaned Mrs Seaton. 'He ate one of my slippers this evening, not to mention three potatoes, a vegetable brush and part of the kitchen doormat.'

They all laughed. 'Puppies like a varied diet,' Toby said lightly.

'He isn't a puppy,' said Mrs Seaton grimly. 'He's a vacuum cleaner. Anything not actually nailed down gets swallowed whole.'

'You'll soon love him,' Elizabeth told her, smiling. 'You know you will!'

'I don't want to,' her mother protested. 'I find dogs a nuisance. They demand too much love and attention.'

'Don't we all?' her husband said quietly.

She looked at him and sighed.

Toby put a record of Spanish guitar music on the record player and began to pour drinks for them all. Jonas came into the room, leaning on his stick, as elegant as Toby in his old-fashioned but well-cut dark suit.

Elizabeth saw him looking at her with a half defiant, half propitiating air, and her heart softened. She went up to him and kissed the lean old cheek, whispering, 'You must have been quite dangerously attractive when you were young, Jonas! You're the best-looking man here tonight as it is!'

He put an arm around her and looked down into her smiling eyes.

'Forgiven me, have you?' he asked gruffly, yet with a tender look.

'I suppose I must have,' she assented softly.

Toby came towards them, pretending to scowl. 'Hey, Jonas, I'm supposed to be the chap who whispers sweet nothings in her ear, not you!'

Dan laughed harshly. 'Supposed to be!' he repeated.

A silence fell. Everyone began to talk at once, and Toby flushed dark red.

Jonas looked sardonically at him. 'No comment, Toby?'

Toby's warm brown eyes were hard as pebbles. He made no answer, but slid his arm around Elizabeth.

'Come up and see Aunt Kate. She's been waiting impatiently for us for hours. She won't be able to stay awake for long, though. We mustn't stay for more than a moment or two. Talking tires her so much.'

Karen was sitting beside Aunt Kate's bed, holding the small, withered fingers in hers. She looked round, smiling. 'Here they are! I told you they'd be up in a second.'

Aunt Kate beamed at them. Her eyes seemed very misty and vague tonight. 'Dan and Liz,' she said softly. 'My dears, I am so pleased.'

Toby opened his mouth, flushing, then stopped, as Elizabeth pinched his arm. She went up to the bed and bent down, smiling into Aunt Kate's drowsy face.

'How are you tonight? You look much better!' It was not true. Aunt Kate looked worn and exhausted.

'Do I?' The faded blue eyes brightened slightly. 'That's good. You look so beautiful, Liz dear. Enjoy your party. I like to hear people enjoying themselves. I wish I could come down to be with you, but I feel a little sleepy.'

'Another time,' Elizabeth nodded.

'Yes, another time. . .' Aunt Kate's eyes closed suddenly, and she began to breathe regularly in sleep.

Karen got up, sighing. 'She keeps dropping off like that, every few minutes. I think the tablets she has to take make her very drowsy.'

'They stop the pain,' Elizabeth said. 'That's the main thing.' She looked affectionately down at the sleeping face. 'I'm glad she's not in pain at the moment.'

Aunt Alice came in quietly. 'Karen, you go down and join the party. I'll stay with her.'

'Are you sure, Mother?' asked Karen hesitantly.

Her mother nodded. She glanced at Elizabeth coldly. Toby frowned.

When they were on their way downstairs, he held Elizabeth's hand. 'My mother doesn't mean to be unkind, you know. I think our little pretence has upset her.'

She nodded. 'I realise that, Toby. She knows the truth now, though? I suppose Jonas told her. He seems to have told everyone else.'

Karen turned and looked at them. 'It was rather unfair to Mother, Toby. She's upset because you lied to her.'

'We did it for Aunt Kate's sake,' Toby snapped. 'It may have been damned silly, but it was well-intentioned.'

'Famous last words,' Karen said sharply.

'Oh, please,' begged Elizabeth, 'what's the point of quarrelling? It's done now.'

Karen shrugged, and said no more. They reached the room in which the party was proceeding to find Doctor Flint talking to James Seaton while Mrs Seaton eyed him grimly.

Karen flushed as she saw the doctor, and sidled away to the other side of the room, then stopped as Tom uncoiled himself from the depths of the most comfortable armchair and greeted her.

Toby changed the record, putting on a record of languorous waltzes, then turned to Elizabeth and invited her to dance. She slid into his outstretched arms and they moved down to the far end of the room, where the carpet had been taken up and the furniture removed, leaving the woodblock flooring perfect for dancing.

'Shall we discard middle age for a while, my dear?' James Seaton said, turning to his wife. 'It's a long time since we danced.' He smiled at Dr Flint. 'Modern dances are not my style. The idea of dancing with your partner without even touching her is abominable.'

'And rather a bar to closer relations,' the doctor

agreed drily. He glanced hopefully at Karen.

Tom took Karen's hand. 'Shall we show them all how it should be done?' he asked her.

She flushed wildly, even her throat and shoulders seeming to grow pink.

'If. . .if you like,' she stammered. 'I'm not very good, though. I. . .perhaps you'd rather dance with someone else?'

Tom laughed. 'Who do you suggest?'

She looked away. 'Oh, silly of me! Of. . .of course, there isn't anyone else here!'

Doctor Flint cleared his throat. 'As the only spare girl you're going to be in demand,' he said. 'We must take it in turns.'

Tom eyed him lazily. 'Oh, no, Flint! It's catch-as-catch-can tonight! I'm not sharing Karen with every other man.'

Karen looked at him in startled surprise, and Elizabeth, catching what he had said, stared at him, then glanced across at Dan. He was sitting beside Jonas, talking to him with absorbed attention, his head bent to catch what his grandfather was saying. He appeared unaware of the small scene which was being acted out on the other side of the room.

Elizabeth glared at her brother, over Toby's shoulder. Tom met her glance with stolid blankness. What was Tom up to? she wondered nervously. Was he trying to keep both Dan and Dr Flint away from Karen? That would do no good. It might have been a good idea for Karen to be thrown into Dr Flint's company, but if she was with Tom she would not be able to see the very real admiration which Dr Flint was showing her.

Irritated, she wondered if Tom was doing this deliberately. He had said that Dr Flint would not suit Karen. Surely he could see that what he was doing now was just as bad as the way in which Jonas and James Seaton had hatched a plot against herself and Dan! It never paid to interfere with other people.

Then she caught herself up. What else was she doing but interfering, or at least hoping it would be possible! She wanted Karen to like Doctor Flint because she wanted to part her from Dan. She was guilty of the same interference, at least in expectation.

Tom and Karen whirled past them, Karen's smooth brown head close to Tom's shoulder, the bright yellow folds of her long dress flowing around her. She had an old-fashioned, rather appealing look. Her dress was deliberately styled to make her look like some Jane Austen character, the high bosom emphasising her new slimness, the beribboned neckline drawing attention to her smooth white skin and slender throat. A locket on a thin gold chain sparkled against her neck, she had pinned a narrow gilt headband across the top of her head.

Elizabeth watched her over Toby's shoulder. She sighed, and Toby glanced down at her.

'What's the matter? You sound very depressed.'

She smiled up at him. 'Do I? I'm not. A little sad, because of Aunt Kate, perhaps.'

Toby's bright eyes watched her. 'Have you thought about my suggestion, Liz? Have you been telling yourself how lovable I am?'

'I don't need to,' she told him gently. 'I've always been very fond of you, Toby—you know that.'

'Fond?' He wrinkled his nose. 'That isn't enough, love. I demand a deathless passion.' His voice was light, but his eyes were not smiling.

She sighed again. 'Oh, well, that does rather ask a lot, doesn't it?' She met Dan's eyes across the room. He was looking perfectly impassive, his blue glance coolly watchful. Turning her head away, she said quietly to Toby, 'I'm afraid I could never give you that sort of love, Toby.'

'Are you certain? It couldn't possibly grow on you?'

'Don't, Toby!' she said abruptly. 'I hate to hurt you. I'd give anything to be able to think of you like that. We've always been so close, haven't we? Too close, Toby. Too much like brother and sister.'

His pixie-like face watched hers closely. The smile had gone from his lips as well as his eyes. 'Not to worry, love. I'm not going to say I'm heart-broken. I think I'm probably the gay troubadour type—love 'em and leave 'em.'

Elizabeth lifted her hand from his shoulder and gently touched his cheek, smiling into his eyes.

'Idiot, Toby!'

'You always say that,' he said easily. 'One day I'm going to find a girl who adores me and doesn't notice what an idiot I am.'

'Of course you will. Hundreds, probably.'

'But not you,' he said softly.

She sighed and put her cheek against his. 'Not me, I'm afraid, Toby dear.'

He turned his head to kiss her lips lightly, brushing them so gently that the touch passed before she could respond. 'Ah, well, it's all part of life's rich pattern, I suppose.'

The record came to an end, and Toby released her, walking across the room to change it. Doctor Flint hovered around Karen and Tom, making light conversation. Karen looked at him with a nervous smile, fingering the long ribbons which fell from her neckline to her waist.

'You look like Little Bo-Peep,' the doctor told her. 'Where are your sheep, though?'

Elizabeth took pity on Karen's bemused stare, and joined the little group.

'Karen, come and help me in the kitchen, will you?' she suggested.

Doctor Flint looked at her disapprovingly. 'Oh, I say, that will leave us with no pretty girls!'

'We won't be long,' Elizabeth told him kindly, smiling. She and Karen went out to the kitchen and began to assemble the various dishes which they had already prepared beforehand; the risotto, kept hot in the oven, with shrimps and chicken mixed with the rice, the sliced cold meats, the cheese, the bowl of mixed salad. They were intending to lay it all out in the dining-room, where everyone could help themselves when they felt like it.

Elizabeth glanced at Karen as they worked. 'I like Doctor Flint,' she said lightly. 'He seems very pleasant.'

Karen's face grew very red. She shot Elizabeth an odd look. 'Oh, do you?' She picked up a bowl of stuffed olives and placed it on one of the trays.

'Don't you?' probed Elizabeth, determined to pursue the subject despite Karen's obvious reluctance to discuss it.

'He. . .he's very kind,' Karen stammered.

'But you don't like him?' insisted Elizabeth.

'It isn't that!' Karen was obviously distressed, but her very emotion made the other girl determined to find out what lay behind her antipathy towards the doctor.

'What is it, then?' she asked, therefore.

Karen hesitated. 'He. . .I. . .we went out together once or twice. I think. . .it sounds conceited, but I think he likes me.'

'I'm sure he does,' Elizabeth said, at once. 'Why shouldn't he? You're pretty and very nice. It seems natural enough.'

'Yes,' Karen admitted. 'But you see, I could never like him as much as. . .well, as much as he wants me to. . .'

Elizabeth went on neatly arranging the various dishes on the trays, ready to carry them into the dining-room. Her heart felt cold and chill. 'Why couldn't you like him that much, Karen?' she asked slowly. It was time, she decided, that the whole thing was brought out into the open.

Karen looked desperately about her, as though looking for help. Her cheeks were glowing bright pink and her eyes were fever-bright. Elizabeth saw that she would have to push her still further. 'Karen,' she said gently, 'I think I know why!'

'Do you?' Karen looked at her, then, in mingled hope and alarm.

'You love someone else? That's it, isn't it?'

Karen smiled nervously and nodded. 'Yes,' she murmured. 'That's it.'

Elizabeth took a deep breath. Her heart was feeling as though it was being put through a mangle, but she was quite determined to make Karen tell her the truth. No more suspicions, no more hope or dread, she thought. Just the plain, unvarnished truth.

'Who, Karen?' she asked bluntly.

Karen looked at her with a small, shy smile. 'You must have guessed! There isn't anyone else.' She sighed. 'He's never even noticed me, of course. Until tonight.' Her eyes glowed with a deep, warm emotion. 'I think he might have taken some notice of me at last, though, after tonight.'

Elizabeth was bewildered. She stared at her, her eyes wide and dazed.

Until tonight? That could not be Dan. He had barely looked at Karen all evening. Unless he had done so before they arrived, of course. But even so, what about that conversation she had overheard?

'Who do you mean, Karen?' she asked harshly. 'I thought it was Dan!'

Karen stared at her in absolute astonishment, her mouth dropping open.

'Dan?' She giggled. 'You couldn't think I was in love with Dan! Why, he's old enough to be my uncle, if not my father!' Her eyes grew round and curious. 'Oh, Liz, that isn't why——?'

Liz flushed. 'Never mind that—who are you in love with, Karen, for God's sake?'

'Why, Tom, of course,' said Karen flatly.

CHAPTER NINE

ELIZABETH dropped a large bowl of chilled potato salad with a resounding crash. She stared down at the floor in confused dismay.

'Oh, lord! What a mess! Aunt Alice will murder me!'

Karen knelt down and began to clear up the mess, her brown head bent so that Elizabeth could not see her face.

'Karen, is it true?' Elizabeth demanded, kneeling beside her and helping to pick up the salad with fingers that shook nervelessly.

'Yes,' Karen admitted, still refusing to look up. 'You won't tell him, will you, Liz? I couldn't bear it if he knew—I'd be so humiliated.'

'Of course I won't breathe a word to him,' Elizabeth said quickly. 'I shouldn't dream of such a thing!' Then her heart rose in her throat like a bubble, and she began to laugh weakly.

'But. . .Tom! And I never suspected for a moment! You've kept your secret very well, Karen.'

'I'm glad,' Karen said simply, standing up as she finished her work of tidying up, and carefully bestowing the potato salad and the broken pieces of the bowl into a sheet of newspaper which she folded into a parcel and put into the disposal bucket.

Elizabeth's thoughts were a tangle of confused emotion and swift thought. Tom and Karen! She did not doubt the other girl for an instant, but the revelation had changed everything.

Her face went suddenly white. She turned and looked at Karen with wide, horrified eyes.

'Karen! I must ask you. One day, several months ago, I overheard you and Dan talking in the garden. You were in tears.' She flushed and looked away from Karen's attentive, puzzled face. 'Dan. . .Dan had his arms round you, comforting you. You were saying something about not wanting to hurt someone, about keeping the truth a secret in case someone should guess!' She paused, shaking violently. She could see the scene now, could feel her own reaction as sharply as she had felt them now.

'Yes?' Karen asked, and when Elizabeth looked at her with searching intensity, she saw no guilt, no fear, in the small, pale face, only a mild curiosity and a faint flicker of quiet grief.

'Who were you talking about?' Elizabeth asked, conscious that her heart seemed to have stopped beating to wait for the answer.

'Why, Aunt Kate,' Karen said at once. She sighed. 'Doctor Flint had just told me the truth. We'd known that Aunt Kate wasn't very well, but we hadn't realised how serious it was—Doctor Flint had just found out himself. He told me, then he told Dan and Jonas.'

Elizabeth closed her eyes. Oh, God, she thought, what have I done?

Karen came to her, put her arms around her in dismay. 'Why, Liz, you look quite ill! What is it?' Then, as it slowly dawned on her. 'Oh, no! You didn't think. . .' She stopped abruptly, working it out. 'You broke your engagement because you thought that Dan and I. . .? Oh, Liz, how awful!'

Elizabeth began to laugh, half hysterically. 'It sounded so suspicious. Can you remember what you said, both of you? You mentioned no names— just talked about feeling guilty and being unhappy in keeping the truth from "her". . .what was I to think? Dan seemed so protective and tender! I leapt to the obvious conclusion!'

Karen stared at her, dumbfounded. 'But, Liz, why didn't you ask Dan? Why not make sure before you acted on it?'

Elizabeth turned away, shrugging her shoulders. 'How could I ask him? If he'd known that I'd found out, I thought it would load you both with a terrible burden of guilt. I was miserable, but I didn't want to do that!' She turned round, smiling at Karen in a strained fashion. 'After all, we all grew up together. I'm very fond of you, Karen, and I. . .loved Dan very much.'

Karen blenched. 'Oh, Liz, how you must have suffered! How brave and generous of you! To think of us after what you thought you'd seen. I don't know how you could have been so self-sacrificing.'

Elizabeth shook her head, grimacing. 'The mood

of noble self-sacrifice didn't last long. I felt I hated you both for quite a time! Don't think I was being a saintly martyr, because I wasn't!'

'I'm surprised you could bear to be polite to me,' Karen said frankly. 'I don't think I could have been so forbearing!'

'I felt like a hypocrite,' Elizabeth admitted. 'My inner thoughts were so poisonous, yet I kept up a pretence of being calm and collected.'

Karen sat down on a chair and stared at her. 'But surely it must have dawned on you that you were mistaken? I mean, Dan and I have never been that close! I've always looked on him as a big brother, almost as an uncle. He's almost twice my age!'

'I'm afraid I thought your apparent indifference to each other was the most horrible sham! And when you confessed to me one day that you'd made a mess of falling in love, then said you couldn't talk to me of all people about it—I obviously thought you were talking about Dan!'

Karen laughed. 'Of course—I can see that! And I was thinking of Tom all the time, not wanting Tom to find out, and being afraid that if I admitted how I felt to you, you'd drop Tom a hint, or somehow let the secret out!'

Elizabeth put her hands to her hot cheeks. 'Oh, Karen!' She had suddenly remembered that she had told Tom her suspicions about Dan. 'I've done something much worse!'

Karen looked startled. 'What?'

'I told Tom about you and Dan!'

Karen went absolutely white, her eyes like hurt brown pools. 'Oh, no! He'll hate me!'

'Karen, I'm sorry! What an appalling mess I've made of it all—with the very best of intentions!'

'What did Tom say?' Karen asked in a parched little voice.

'He was stunned.' Elizabeth looked at her thoughtfully. 'And not very pleased, now I come to think of it. He seemed rather annoyed, and said that you must be out of your skull to get involved with Dan, because he was totally wrong for you.'

'I wonder what he meant?' Karen looked at her, a small hint of pink creeping back into her white cheeks.

'I'm not sure,' Elizabeth admitted. 'But his attitude to you tonight looks hopeful, doesn't it?'

Karen sighed, her shoulders drooping. 'I thought so at the time, but now I see that it was probably just Tom's way of trying to help you. He was most likely trying to keep me away from Dan, trying to protect you!'

Elizabeth did not feel that she could argue with that. It had occurred to her, too. Tom was quite capable of doing just that.

Karen pinned a bright smile to her pale mouth. 'Well, anyway, at least some good has come out of it! You can go to Dan and tell him the truth now, get engaged again.'

Elizabeth looked at her with dull regret. 'No, Karen, I can't do that.'

'But, surely, now you realise you were wrong—' Karen protested in surprise.

'Put yourself in Dan's place! He would be furious.' Elizabeth shook her head. 'No, I can't tell him.' She flushed. 'It would look very like a request to be taken back.'

'Don't you want to marry him?' Karen asked simply.

Elizabeth sighed. 'It's not that simple. Promise me, Karen, that you won't breathe a word to him, or anyone else?'

'But, Elizabeth. . .'

'Promise,' she repeated firmly.

Karen sighed. 'I can hardly refuse you, can I? Very well, I promise, but I'm sure you're making a mistake.'

'Karen, I broke my engagement to Dan because I misunderstood something I overheard. If I go to Dan now and tell him that, he'll first of all be furious that I didn't trust him enough to ask him outright, then he'll have the choice of either asking me to marry him again, or refusing to do so. Either way, he's being pushed, don't you see that? It would be humiliating for me if he told me to get lost, and even if he immediately suggested we got engaged again, I would never be sure he hadn't done it because he felt he had to!'

Karen looked at her blankly. 'You make it sound so complicated. Surely you owe it to Dan to tell him the truth?'

Elizabeth winced. That was true, she thought.

She had totally misjudged Dan, wronged him unforgivably.

'Is it your pride, Liz?' Karen asked gently. 'I can understand it if it is—I have my pride, too. I've held it to me like a shield whenever I saw Tom, or thought about him. It was a great comfort to me at times. I would have died if Tom had ever found out how I felt about him.'

'I suppose,' Elizabeth said slowly, 'pride is part of it. But there are other aspects. I. . .I want to be sure Dan loves me. I want him to come freely to me, without feeling pressured into it.'

Karen looked uneasily at her. 'Liz, what about Toby?'

'Toby?' Elizabeth sounded taken aback, vague, puzzled.

Karen watched her face, trying to see the emotions which lay at the back of the slanting green eyes.

'Yes,' she said slowly. 'Do you feel anything for Toby?'

The door opened in the middle of her question, and Dan stood there, looking from one to the other of them with a sardonic, cynical air.

'Yes,' he repeated mockingly, 'do you, Liz?'

She flushed hotly and turned with haste to pick up one of the loaded trays.

'Have you come to help us carry the food? Good. Here you are, take this one.' And she pushed the tray into his automatically outstretched hands.

He looked at her over it, his firm mouth lifting at

the corner in an amused, intimate smile.

'Some time soon you're going to have to answer that question, Liz! Run while you can.'

When he had gone, Karen looked at Elizabeth with a small smile.

'I don't think you'll need your pride much longer, Liz. Dan isn't the man to be pressured into anything! He's always known what he wanted, and gone after it ruthlessly.'

'He let me go without a murmur,' Liz pointed out dully.

Karen frowned. 'Did he? I wonder why!'

They followed Dan, walking slowly with their heavy trays, and when all the food had been elegantly arranged on the table, went back to the party to inform the others that the cold buffet was ready for them.

'At last!' grumbled Jonas. 'It took you long enough!'

Dan helped him to his feet. Doctor Flint joined Karen and looked at her hard.

'I hope we're going to have that dance later,' he said. 'I've hardly seen anything of you tonight.'

She lowered her head, flushing, her lashes sweeping down on her pink cheeks in a fine dark crescent.

Tom came up behind her and took her elbow. He looked at the other man, smiling politely.

'I'll take you to supper, shall I, Karen? You can help me fill my plate. Did you make your famous risotto tonight? I love that. I always try to get lots of shrimps in my portion—the mixture of shrimps and rice just suits me.'

Dr Flint scowled as Tom neatly detached Karen and marched her out of the door, then he dived after them.

Elizabeth watched, amused. Karen was going to have a charming evening, being squabbled over by two very personable young men. Perhaps the sight of opposition had at last awakened Tom to a sense of Karen's value.

It was sufficiently revealing that he should be prepared to go to so much trouble on her behalf. His normal easy-going temper had been almost laid aside tonight. Of course, they had always been so close. Tom had taken her for granted, no doubt. Now he would realise that if he did not move fast he would lose her.

The very idea of Tom moving fast was enough to make Elizabeth chuckle. What love could do to people! It could almost alter their whole nature, at least temporarily!

She started as Dan came back into the room and looked at her coolly, one dark eyebrow raised in quizzical enquiry.

'Not coming in to eat?'

'Yes,' she said hastily. 'I'm just coming.'

He caught her wrist as she tried to dive past him, and held her, at arm's length, looking sardonically into her eyes.

'Not yet!' He leaned over and deftly switched on the stereo, still holding her tethered by one hand. A slow, sweet tune swirled out on the air.

Dan turned back. His hand slid slowly round her waist, he pulled her into his arms, his other hand running up her arm to her shoulder.

'We haven't danced for a long time,' he said.

She stood, rooted to the spot. 'Since the cricket club dance,' she nodded, her eyes lifted to his.

'When Toby kissed you,' he said in a cool voice.

Her cheeks burned bright pink. 'Yes!'

'Will you dance with me, Liz?' he asked, half pleadingly, half in challenge, crooking an eyebrow upwards.

She let him take her hand. Her heart beat so rapidly that she was certain he would hear it, and know the emotion which was consuming her.

She glanced up at him, from under her lashes, and saw his face, calmly complacent as he gazed across the room. Suddenly she remembered what her father and Jonas had said about Dan. Was any of it true? Had Dan always ridden roughshod over her, domineered, imposed his own will?

Yes, she thought, of course they're right. Dan is self-willed, arrogant, assertive, and he would have tried to rule me, as he has always ruled the factory, with a hand of iron. I would have realised all this long ago if the velvet glove hadn't been so damnably attractive.

She saw now that the conversation she had overheard between him and Karen had only been the last straw. She had already been strained to breaking point by his arbitrary behaviour. It was unjust to blame her father for that long engagement. If she had married Dan at once, they would have reached the same point sooner or later, because his nature was built for tyranny. The real trouble was that he had never come up against any powerful opposition, except from Jonas, and the old man was too amused by Dan's carbon copy of his own domineering ways to have tried seriously to put on the brake, until it was too late.

But I love Dan just the same, she thought helplessly. What can I do? My love makes me weak. Her pride rose in rebellion. You can take Jonas's advice, she told herself scathingly. Give Dan a fight before it's too late. If he really loves you, he'll compromise. Love is the answer as well as the problem.

He looked down at her, smiling triumphantly. 'Shall we start again, Liz? Forget the past?'

She looked at him through her lashes. 'How do you mean?'

He flickered a long, desirous glance over her. 'I'm prepared to forget about your little fling with Toby.'

'Are you, Dan?' she asked very softly.

He put his hand under her chin and tipped back her head. A little spark kindled at the back of the blue eyes as they surveyed her.

'You're very lovely, Liz,' he said huskily. 'Yes, I can forget about Toby—perhaps I was a little to blame. I left you too much alone. You were bored, and Toby was always around.' His lips curled angrily. 'I should have pushed his face through the back of his head when I began to suspect what he was doing, but I was so damned angry to think that you could even look at him!'

'Were you?' she asked in the same sweet tone.

He looked at her quickly, frowning. 'I have my pride, Liz!'

'Yes,' she agreed, 'you certainly have!'

His face tightened and his eyes narrowed. 'Are you making fun of me, damn you?'

She lifted her eyes to his in an innocent gaze, the slanting green depths quite empty of expression.

'I wouldn't dare, Dan!'

'You don't still care about Toby, do you?' he demanded. 'Is that what's behind that face of yours? When I flew out to Italy I intended to find out exactly what the situation was—I soon realised that whatever there had been between you, it was no longer in existence. You were flirting with Italians and Toby seemed incapable of coping. Oh, I saw he was jealous. You had him on a string all right. But you'd lost interest, or so I imagined.'

'I thought you came to Italy for Aunt Kate's sake,' she pointed out reasonably.

He lifted his shoulders in a shrug. 'I did, of course—that was a secondary reason.'

'Killing two birds with one stone, Dan? How economical of you!'

The blue eyes were fixed on her face, intent and wary. 'You sound very aloof. What do you want me to say? I've admitted I still want to marry you, still find you attractive. I came to Italy in pursuit of you. Doesn't that mean anything?'

She put her head on one side. 'Yes,' she said slowly, her tone full of thoughtful irony. 'It means you never know when you're beaten, Dan. But I already knew that.'

His lips drew in tightly. 'Why are you sniping at me like this? What the hell's the matter with you? You aren't in love with Toby!' Then, looking sharply at her, and with an oddly repressed intonation, 'Are you, Liz?'

Calmly she shook her head. 'No, and I never was in love with him. I've behaved abominably to Toby, used him for my own purposes without shame.'

He grinned, letting out a long sigh of relief. 'I knew it!' His hands dropped on her shoulders, shook her slightly, as he bent forward, smiling with all his not inconsiderable charm at her. 'Liz! I want you, you know that!' He bent and kissed her hard, but briefly, lifting his head to smile at her. 'And you love me—I can't believe you don't!'

She stepped back swiftly, and his hands dropped away. He stared at her, frowning.

'Do you ever listen to yourself, Dan? Do you ever hear what you're saying? You tell me you want me. Note that word. *Want!* And then you have the unutterable nerve to insist that I *love* you—and say you can't believe I don't love you.' Her eyes darted contempt at him. 'There's all the world between those two words, Dan! Wanting and loving aren't the same thing. And I'm afraid, until you know the difference, and can honestly offer me a little more than the pleasure of being the object of your temporary needs, then I want no more to do with you!' She turned on her heel as she finished, and walked out of the room.

She joined the others, her face very flushed, and helped herself to a great deal of food which she could not have felt less like eating.

Jonas, seated on a hard-backed chair, slowly consuming a few slices of cold ham, looked at her with some interest, and crooked a finger for her, in his regal and arrogant way.

Elizabeth went over to him, lifting an amused brow. 'Well, Jonas? What do you want with me now?'

He shot her a sharp look. 'Aha! You have a very elated look tonight, my girl. What's going on?' His glance moved over her shoulder to the door, scrutinising Dan, who had just entered the room, and was standing staring at Elizabeth's back with a hard, unsmiling face.

A satisfied smile dawned on Jonas's face. 'Gone away, Liz?' he asked teasingly. 'Playing fox and hounds with Dan? That's the idea!'

She gave him an affectionate, ironic look. 'You have all the instincts of the sadist, Jonas! I'm ashamed of you!'

'Nonsense!' he said cheerfully. 'The boy was riding for a fall.' He lifted her hand and kissed the back of it with a courtly gesture. 'I envy him, I don't mind admitting! You're not only very pretty, you're a spirited little creature. Give him a run for his money, Liz! Give him a run for his money!'

She grinned at him, shaking her head. 'Thank you for the advice, Jonas, but will you let me handle my own affairs? I'm a big girl now!'

Doctor Flint was hovering at Karen's elbow, she saw, as she looked across the room. Karen was nervously nibbling at her food, very pink and bright-eyed, for all the world like a shy little squirrel. Tom was calmly talking to her, ingoring the doctor, but Elizabeth guessed, from Karen's glazed expression, that she was barely able to take in what he said because of her extreme tension.

James Seaton walked across to speak to Elizabeth, his eyes as curious as Jonas's had been, and praised the food. 'The risotto is particularly well made!'

'You must tell Karen that, not me, Dad. I'm not responsible for that. It is good, isn't it? Karen has a very clever pair of hands.' She looked at her father with hidden amusement, wondering what his re-action would be if Tom married Karen. Would he be pleased? For once, she thought delightedly, the clever and omniscient men of the family were entirely in the dark! None of them had any idea of Karen's secret, and when the light did break, they would be stunned.

Toby popped up, grinning at her, apparently restored to his normal cheerful humour. She smiled back, relieved to see him so much himself. She had feared she had hurt him badly, but as she met the dancing brown eyes, and saw the impish smile curl the corners of his mouth, she dismissed the notion. Toby was too light-hearted. Whatever he had felt for her, it had not gone very deep. A surface attraction, complicated by long friendship; that was all it had been, she reassured herself.

'You aren't eating much. Not hungry? Then come back and dance,' he invited. 'The night is young yet. Or shall we go up and visit Aunt Kate?'

'No,' she said firmly. 'She should be fast asleep by now. We won't disturb her again tonight. Let's dance, Toby.'

He took her hand, put her plate down on the buffet table and drew her back into the other room. Dan, leaning against the wall by the door, watched them pass, his face a cool mask. Toby gave him a wicked, bright-eyed, taunting grin as he passed, and Elizabeth, following Toby's glance, saw, deep within Dan's hard blue eyes, a blaze of anger briefly leap up, then die away before the lids dropped to cover his expression.

When they were back in the other room, Toby looked at her with a smile, then twisted his neck, pretending to look at his own back. 'Can you see it?'

She was briefly puzzled. 'See what?'

'The dagger Dan just stuck between my ribs,' he said jauntily.

'Idiot!' she retorted, laughing.

Toby bent a suddenly sober look on her. 'My love, one day you'll call me that once too often!'

She was instantly serious. 'I'm sorry! Do you

mind, really? Of course, I won't use it again if you
do, but it's meant with complete affection, Toby.'

His brown eyes smiled down into hers. 'I know!
Take no notice. I was just flying up into the boughs!
I like the way you say it—really!' He darted off to
put a record on the turntable, came back and held
out his arms. 'Dance, dance, dance, little lady!' he
said gaily, and she laughingly came into his arms.

CHAPTER TEN

ELIZABETH woke up the following morning to a world of bright, cool sunshine. She lay, smiling, staring up at the ceiling. A feeling of intense excitement filled her as she went back over the events of the day before. She had managed to avoid Dan for the rest of the evening, but he had been permanently in the background, his gaze intent, while she danced with Toby or Doctor Flint, and she had always been aware of him.

Then her smile died. What if he doesn't love me? she asked herself. What if it really is just a physical need? She leapt out of bed and went to the window, to banish such pessimistic thoughts.

The green was vanishing from the trees. A pale gold had taken its place, with here and there the crisp tinge of russet or brown, or the sudden flame of a maple. Cobwebs blew gently in the morning breeze, glistening with dew, like diamonds caught in lace. The sky was clear and very blue, but in the distance a few clouds moved ponderously along, like sheep driven over rough ground. Autumn, she thought, sniffing the air, which already seemed laden with smoke, a pleasantly acrid scent of bonfires. The lawn was littered with dry, curled leaves. Asters and chrysanthemums gave colour to the flower beds. The golden rod stood in thick lines at the side of the garden shed.

She went to the bathroom, came back and dressed quickly. Wearing a vivid green shirt and fawn skirt, she went down to breakfast, humming.

Tom was just finishing his meal as she joined him. He stood up, smiling. 'I'm late—I must hurry. Oh, Mum, I shan't be in for supper tonight. I'm taking Karen to the cinema.'

Mrs Seaton nodded without taking much notice, but Elizabeth looked up sharply at her brother.

He winked at her and went out. Thoughtfully, Elizabeth ate her grapefruit and nibbled half a slice of toast. Mrs Seaton was compiling a shopping list with an abstracted expression.

The telephone rang a few moments later, and Mrs Seaton said plaintively, 'Take that, will you, Liz? I'm busy.'

It was Jonas, his voice a little shaky but sounding quite calm.

'Liz? Kate died in her sleep last night. I thought you'd like to know.'

She closed her eyes briefly. 'Oh, no!'

'It was much the best way,' he said gently. 'She looked very peaceful. Is your father still there?'

'No, he's already gone to the factory. Is there anything I can do to help, Jonas?'

'No, my dear, nothing at all, thank you. We can manage. Do you think you could ring your father for me, though? Tell him what's happened, and say that I won't be coming in today. Nor will Dan, of course.'

'Of course,' she said. 'I'll ring him at once.'

Mrs Seaton looked up as Elizabeth came slowly back in to the room.

'What is it?' Then, swiftly, 'Kate?'

Elizabeth nodded. 'In her sleep. Very peacefully, Jonas says. I rang Dad and told him. Jonas and Dan are not going in to work today, so Dad will have to stay late tonight.'

Mrs Seaton stared at the kitchen table. A tear ran slowly down her cheek. 'I've known Kate Woodham for so long!' she said huskily. 'She's been the best of friends to me!'

Elizabeth put an arm around her, patting her shoulder. 'I know, Mum! We all loved Aunt Kate.'

'Poor Jonas—how he'll miss her!' said Mary Seaton.

Elizabeth looked at her doubtfully. 'Do you think so? Jonas has always seemed so self-sufficient to me.'

'He probably doesn't even realise how much he's always relied on Kate. His wife was a very negative sort of woman, you know. She was terrified of Jonas. He was kind to her, but in a rather scornful way, I believe. Kate had to run the house even then, and for all her gentleness Kate could always find the courage to tell Jonas when he was wrong.'

Elizabeth sat down and stared thoughtfully at the garden. The curtains blew gently in the breeze. She could see the tops of the trees, the last roses of

summer on the rambling bushes along the trellis,
their outer leaves brown and shrivelled, but still
retaining their inner colour.

Was that what Jonas had wanted for Dan? A
woman who would tell him when he was wrong?

Tom arrived back early, as usual. Karen had had
to cancel their date, he told Elizabeth. She was
helping her mother with the necessary arrangements. Jonas had decreed that they should not go
into mourning for Kate, except briefly for the
funeral, which was to take place in three days' time.

A week later, Toby strolled through the copse to
visit Elizabeth, a purposeful look in his brown eyes.
She was kneeling beside the massed chrysanthemums, tying them securely to stakes. The
previous night a storm had blown up. It had raged
for hours, making havoc in the flower borders,
tearing one great limb from a beech tree on the edge
of the copse and leaving the exposed trunk white
and ragged, knocking down a tile from the gable of
the roof and generally keeping the family awake for
hours.

Elizabeth looked up as Toby joined her, and
smiled. 'How did you sleep? Wasn't that wind
terrible?'

'I was glad I wasn't at sea,' he agreed lightly. 'I
came to say goodbye, Liz.'

She stiffened, her fingers very still on the strips of
green twine she was using as ties. 'Goodbye?' she
repeated slowly.

'I'm winging back to Italy,' he said.

She looked up at him, sitting back on her heels. 'Alone?'

His eyes were gentle. 'You aren't coming with me, are you, Liz?'

'Is that a statement—or question?'

'Whichever you prefer!'

She hesitated. 'Who decided it was time you went back?'

He pushed his hands into his pockets and rocked to and fro, his lips pursed. 'Who do you think?'

'Dan?'

He looked down into her face with a wry smile. 'Who else?'

'And he also decided that I wasn't going with you?' Her temper was rising. She kept her voice very even, but her eyes snapped up at Toby, sparks flying from them.

'Was there any doubt on the subject?' Toby said reasonably.

Elizabeth dropped her handful of green twine and stood up. 'I'm not going to be dictated to by anyone,' she said sharply. 'It's up to me to make up my own mind. Dan didn't ask me what I wanted to do—he just went ahead and arranged matters without consulting me. It's time the great Dan Woodham discovered that he's not God Almighty!'

Toby stood, watching her as she walked fast across the grass and disappeared into the copse. A sigh shook him and he kicked idly at a clump of grass.

The puppy, crawling out from the hiding place he had delightedly discovered behind the garden shed, advanced on his stomach, wriggling and wagging his tail.

'Hello, Charlie!' Toby murmured, crouching to fondle his soft ears. 'Your mistress has just gone storming off to tackle the great Dan Woodham. You and I are casualties in that battle, I'm afraid, pup.'

Peering up at him from a tangle of brown hair, the puppy sympathetically licked his hand.

'Ah, you recognise a fellow victim,' Toby told him lightly. He gave him a final pat and stood up. 'Well, Charlie, it has to be hello and goodbye, I'm afraid. We must find what comfort we can, you in your small corner, I in mine.' Then he strolled off, leaving the little dog to chase his tail in ever decreasing circles on the lawn until he tumbled, panting, in a heap and went off with happy innocence to sleep.

Elizabeth walked into the garden of Whitebriars at steam-engine speed, her chin up in preparation for battle.

Dan sat on the paved patio outside the french windows, in a cane chair, reading a newspaper. He laid it aside as she advanced, and leaned back, his scrutiny cool and unsurprised.

'Did you tell Toby I wouldn't be going back to Italy?' she demanded as she came up to him.

'I did,' Dan drawled.

Her eyes flashed. 'How dare you? I make my own decisions, and if I want to go to Italy, I shall! Who do you think you are, riding roughshod over people, ruling their lives as though you were God, never caring twopence for what they think or want. . .'

Dan stood up and caught her by the arms, jerking her up against him, his smile derisive. 'Stop talking, you little shrew!'

She pushed at his chest indignantly, then as his mouth covered hers in a hard, demanding kiss, her words died on her lips.

Her arms went up round his neck, she relaxed and gave herself up to the intense pleasure of his kiss, feeling her own heart beating fiercely and his answering with a hard, rapid thunder.

When he drew back and looked down into her face her eyes were dreamy, her lips parted in a sigh of contentment.

'I hate you,' she told him.

'So I gather,' he murmured wickedly. 'I wondered if you'd ever come to me. In the end I had to be as unscrupulous as you are, my love, and use Toby as my goad.'

She looked up, then, her brows jerking together in a frown. 'What?'

'I knew, when I told Toby you weren't coming back with him, that he would tell you at once.' Dan grinned shamelessly. 'I watched him walk across the copse, and then I sat down here and waited. It took about five minutes. The longest five minutes of my life, I may add.'

'You. . .you. . .' words failed her, she raised her hand to slap him, but he caught it and held it in an iron grip.

'No violence, my love. Two can play at that game. You demand equality! All right—but that means that if you hit me, I hit you back. I've put up with plenty of physical punishment from you in the past, and done nothing in retaliation. From now on, beware! I'll be unmerciful, I promise you!'

She looked at him in choked wrath. 'I meant what I said to you last time, Dan. It isn't enough to want me. I'm not just an object, like an antique vase or a new car. I'm a person.'

His glance skimmed indolently over her, bright with amusement and appreciation. 'So you are,' he murmured. 'A very pretty person, if I may say so!'

'Why won't you take me seriously?' she wailed.

'What do you want me to say?' he parried, still smiling, but with a curious, leaping flame at the back of his eyes that made her breath catch suddenly. 'That I'm madly in love with you, can't live without you? That I'm reduced to the position of total abjection, trailing at your chariot wheels? Would all that satisfy your vanity and your pride?'

'Dan,' she said, looking at him soberly, 'all I want is for you to say you love me. Not want me, or find me attractive. Just love me. . . it's quite simple!'

He took her hands in his, turned them over and scrutinised them with unsmiling intentness, then slowly lifted them and kissed the palms, his dark head bent in an uncharacteristic humility which took her breath away.

'I love you, Liz,' he said gently. 'I've loved you for so long that I didn't even think it necessary to tell you. I thought you must know how I felt, how I've always felt about you. There are so many things bound up in my love. I loved you as a fat, naughty toddler, throwing your birthday cake at me in a tantrum. I loved you as a freckle-faced monkey of eight, cheating at Snakes and Ladders. I loved you most of all when you came back from London so beautiful that I could hardly take my eyes off you. If I rushed you off your feet it was out of sheer terror that someone else would get there first.'

She swayed towards him, weak with relief and love, and he caught her and held her hard against him.

'Darling, darling,' she whispered, stroking the back of his head with tender fingers, 'I couldn't have borne it if you hadn't loved me!'

'I can't understand how you could ever doubt it,' he said, kissing her ear and her cheek between the words.

She hesitated, then told him about the overheard conversation, her belief that he loved Karen, her subsequent decision not to divulge her knowledge and the breaking of her engagement.

He listened, watching her impassively. Then he took her face in his hands and pinched her chin, his eyes biting at her.

'You silly little fool! Eavesdroppers never hear anything pleasant, didn't you know that? You might have totally ruined both our lives with your witless, chivalrous leaping to conclusions.' Then he laughed. 'Karen, of all people! Little Karen, who couldn't say boo to a goose! How could you imagine it? I ought to beat you soundly.'

'You let me go so easily, though,' she protested at once. 'I was surprised when you showed no relief, I admit, but your attitude still baffles me. If you loved me, why let me go without so much as a murmur?'

His face was hard with remembered bitterness. 'I'm a very possessive and jealous man, Liz. I knew Toby liked you, I saw how much you liked him. You were thrown together so often while I was busy, and gradually I began to suspect. . .' He shrugged. 'By the time I realised the danger, I thought it was too late. You'd changed. Our relationship was brittle; we quarrelled so often, were irritable with each other. I was afraid to put any pressure on in case I precipitated a final break. I decided to get rid of Toby, send him to Italy—I hoped that that would help. Once he was out of the way, things would return to normal. Then you broke off our engagement, and I thought I'd lost you. I loved you. I was too stunned, at first, to think straight. I had to let you go to Toby, if that was what you wanted.'

She touched his cheek with one finger, feeling the tension of the muscles. He caught her hand and held it against his mouth, moving his lips over her palm.

'And then you changed your mind?' she asked.

He nodded. 'Once the first shock was over, I couldn't rest until I had found out if it was possible to get you back. I flew to Italy, saw at once that there was very little between you and Toby, and from then on I was hopeful of winning you back.'

'Your modesty is staggering,' she mocked.

He smiled. 'My love, your reactions to me were far too violent for any pretence of indifference. I could fight hostility. I could beat down armed dislike. I confess, I wasn't hopeful at first. You held me off for a long time. But then I felt I was breaking through the barriers. After I'd kissed you I was sure of it—your whole body betrayed you.'

She smiled at him, her green eyes alight with laughter and passion. 'I know I gave myself away. I was furious at the time.'

'You were furious *all* the time,' he emphasised. 'Liz, I love you most when your green eyes flash like a cat's, and you stare at me with your red hair almost standing on end. We may not be in for a peaceful life, but, my God, it will be an eventful one!'

She looked up at him through her lashes, her eyes thoughtful and a little teasing.

'And you'll never try to dictate to me again, or ignore my protests, or lay down the law despite my wishes?'

Dan's blue eyes were amused, the clean lines of

his face full of tender humour.

'Oh, I doubt I shall become a reformed man overnight, my dearest. I'm a Woodham, Jonas's grandson. It's in my blood. But I do promise you this—if ever you're determined to stop me in my tracks, you have one unfailing weapon.'

Her eyes filled with laughter. 'Oh? What's that?'

Dan bent his head and kissed her, first gently, then with a mounting passion which surprised and enchanted her. She sighed her abandonment of thought and gave herself up to the hard possession of his arms without another qualm.

Four brand new romances from favourite
Mills & Boon authors have been specially
selected to make your Christmas special.

THE FINAL SURRENDER
Elizabeth Oldfield

SOMETHING IN RETURN
Karen van der Zee

HABIT OF COMMAND
Sophie Weston

CHARADE OF THE HEART
Cathy Williams

Published in November 1992   Price: £6.80

*Available from Boots, Martins, John Menzies, W.H. Smith,
most supermarkets and other paperback stockists.
Also available from Mills & Boon Reader Service, PO Box 236,
Thornton Road, Croydon, Surrey CR9 3RU.*

Next Month's Romances

Each month you can choose from a wide variety of romance with Mills & Boon. Below are the new titles to look out for next month, why not ask either Mills & Boon Reader Service or your Newsagent to reserve you a copy of the titles you want to buy — just tick the titles you would like and either post to Reader Service or take it to any Newsagent and ask them to order your books.

Please save me the following titles:	Please tick	√
BACHELOR AT HEART	Roberta Leigh	
TIDEWATER SEDUCTION	Anne Mather	
SECRET ADMIRER	Susan Napier	
THE QUIET PROFESSOR	Betty Neels	
ONE-NIGHT STAND	Sandra Field	
THE BRUGES ENGAGEMENT	Madeleine Ker	
AND THEN CAME MORNING	Daphne Clair	
AFTER ALL THIS TIME	Vanessa Grant	
CONFRONTATION	Sarah Holland	
DANGEROUS INHERITANCE	Stephanie Howard	
A MAN FOR CHRISTMAS	Annabel Murray	
DESTINED TO LOVE	Jennifer Taylor	
AN IMAGE OF YOU	Liz Fielding	
TIDES OF PASSION	Sally Heywood	
DEVIL'S DREAM	Nicola West	
HERE COMES TROUBLE	Debbie Macomber	

If you would like to order these books in addition to your regular subscription from Mills & Boon Reader Service please send £1.70 per title to: Mills & Boon Reader Service, P.O. Box 236, Croydon, Surrey, CR9 3RU, quote your Subscriber No:........................... (If applicable) and complete the name and address details below. Alternatively, these books are available from many local Newsagents including W.H.Smith, J.Menzies, Martins and other paperback stockists from 4th December 1992.

Name:..

Address:...

....Post Code:........................

To Retailer: If you would like to stock M&B books please contact your regular book/magazine wholesaler for details.

You may be mailed with offers from other reputable companies as a result of this application.
If you would rather not take advantage of these opportunities please tick box ☐